A COLLECTOR OF PHOTOGRAPHS

By the same author

UNORTHODOX METHODS

A COLLECTOR OF PHOTOGRAPHS

Deborah Valentine

LONDON
VICTOR GOLLANCZ LTD
1989

First published in Great Britain 1989
by Victor Gollancz Ltd,
14 Henrietta Street, London WC2E 8QJ

Published by arrangement with Bantam Books,
a division of Bantam Doubleday Dell Publishing
Group, Inc.

British Library Cataloguing in Publication Data
Valentine, Deborah
A collector of photographs.
I. Title
823'.94[F]

ISBN 0-575-04464-0

Printed in Great Britain by
St Edmundsbury Press Ltd, Bury St Edmunds, Suffolk

To Janet Linville

With applause to Michael for his patience

Chapter One

■

September 16—

Espresso. I could do it in tempera. A dark charcoal set against off-white; the white a spiderweb of insignificant cracks in a style a Venetian glassmaker would have called craquelure. In the center of the darkness would be a pinpoint of reflected light, as there was at that moment, superimposing my portrait into the shallowness. I lifted the cup to drink from it; the reflection grew large, then disappeared.

The taste was bitter. I am not fond of espresso; that was why I had ordered it. My reluctance to drink it would make it last a long time, and I could sit where I was, excused and unmolested. I ordered a pastry and then absently dissected it, separating layers of cream and flaky crust into opposing heaps on the plate. I could imagine them a still life done in delicate oils—not by me, but by a Flemish master; touched with varnish, adding a sensuousness to the hues of orange and beige.

The restaurant I chose had a brass rod across the windows, dividing it into halves. Above, uncluttered window; below, hang-

ing from large brass rings, blue curtains. I sat at a break in those curtains so that from that slim opening I could see the building across the street. The window that concerned me was dark, but the draperies were open. The various lights of this busy street, dimly absorbed by the glass, made the figure there easy to see. He was naked from the waist up, his hands laced behind his head; a pose that emphasized the cobra shape of his torso. Pink and yellow from the neon lights of a saloon streaked his chest and caught one side of his hair, missing his face until he stretched forward. I saw the scene in watercolors; darkly soaked around the outer limits, the slashes of pink and yellow so viciously fluorescent they mutilated his features.

He was paid for his beautiful torso. In the morning, he posed for our group of artists, those preferring a collective environment or too poor to afford a private model. In the evenings he was paid for on the streets, also by those seeking inspiration. And then, in between, there was us.

It had never happened to me before—this willingness to be used, this desire to incorporate someone else into my life. Oh, I had married. Because the man was good, because he loved me, because he supported my caprices, my work. Because it never occurred to me there might be any other reason for sharing my life with a man. My husband is a wonderful audience for my many performances; and I, in turn, am a wonderful performer. I can audition the gamut of womanly experience as the situation dictates. Entertaining. Amusing. Sincere. Seductive. Anything in between. Beyond: intelligence, independence, perceptiveness. I do them all exceptionally well. Paul applauds. He indulges. He encourages. He ignores: the occasional taunts, the detachment I think he senses even in our closest moments.

My attention was distracted by an old silver Bentley as it rolled by, dented on one side, headlight out on the other. The occupants were caught by a streetlight. Like a photograph, the man in top hat, the woman with something fuzzy around her shoulder, the chauffeur stiff and dignified. The man and woman were laughing. I could see it clearly, a platinum print displayed in the San Francisco Museum of Modern Art. They passed out of sight. I returned to my window-gazing just as the figure stepped back. I strained to see, but someone pulled the drapes. Not him. I could see him as the fabric ebbed and flowed and obscured him from sight. His partner. I saw the draperies done in acrylic. White on white—oh, what expert shadowing it would take! And I could do it, expose it—give it focus. *I smiled, thinking of it. I had to go home and begin. It would be the first of my new series, whatever the consequences.*

The waiter brought a small ebony tray containing my change and my stub, but I left them both. Outside I had to step quickly back onto the doorstep of the restaurant, where, hidden, I watched two men emerge from a narrow stairway. Not speaking, they went in separate directions, one to the crowded end of the street where young and middle-aged men frequented noisy places, the other to the end of picturesque homes and genteel loneliness. I stayed huddled against the door casing until they were out of sight.

Chapter Two

■

"I don't want to go," Bryce said.

Katharine was leaning against the window, one hand in the bend of Bryce's arm. "God, it's amazing that planes can take off in this weather," she said.

He wondered if she'd heard him. Airports are noisy places, even airports in Ireland. Terrible acoustics. Anxious crowds. Machinery in motion. Or maybe she simply did not know how to reply. Either way, he felt foolish. He put his hands in the pockets of his coat and played with the lint and scraps of paper collected in the seam. When he arrived in San Francisco, he should have it cleaned, he thought.

"You'll be back in time for Christmas?" Katharine asked.

"I should hope so. I've only made reservations until next Friday."

He heard her sigh as she let go of him. Why had she gotten him into this?

"Do you think I'm bored?" he had asked her the previous evening.

She had shrugged as she washed her hands. They were in her studio. She had been executing a study of a bust that was, as yet, unidentifiable to Kevin Bryce.

"Maybe a little," she had said. "But not dangerously so. You have to go to San Francisco anyway, don't you? Couldn't hurt, could it?"

Couldn't it?

The announcement of his flight came over the loudspeaker, drawing him back to the present. Before he boarded, she kissed him good-bye. It was a half-assed sort of kiss, Bryce decided. He felt compelled to look over his shoulder once, and caught nothing but a glance of her sweatered back.

It had started with a letter. Two letters, to be completely accurate. Both from San Francisco. The first, short and to the point, was from Petter Swensen.

> Have a buyer for your Lake Tahoe residence. Can you come to San Francisco to work out some details and sign papers? Would be quicker.
>
> Petter

The second was longer, more oblique in purpose, and addressed to Katharine. It was from a man.

"A really lovely man." Katharine, no people-lover, had been enthusiastic. "Paul Gautier. His wife and I took classes together years ago. She is a very fine artist."

She had read the letter at breakfast without comment; folded the paper and put it away somewhere upstairs while Bryce sat at the table and played with the crumbs on his plate.

Once in the air, a stewardess brought Bryce a scotch and soda. She smiled at him, and it crossed his mind that she was pretty before he turned to stare out the window.

"Katharine," he had protested, "I don't *do* that sort of thing. Didn't you explain to him that I am no longer in law enforcement, and that I was never a private investigator?"

"Yes," she said, rubbing her hand with the towel, drying each finger thoroughly. "I think he wants someone to talk to, and from what I told him, he thought you might be the most... appropriate."

"Katharine," he answered, "the man has a wife whose activities are suspicious, correct? Forgive me for saying so, but it sounds as if he's worried that she's screwing someone else behind his back. I do not slink behind trees with a camera. That is not, and never has been, my business.

"Of course not. But I believe that Paul is worried about more than whether Roxanne is just 'screwing around,' as you so charmingly put it." She paused. "We have an artist whose husband finds not only her activities but her canvases increasingly disturbing."

"So?" he had countered. "We have a man who does not understand the artistic flights of fancy of his spouse. What is so interesting about that? What sets him apart from all the other slightly confused men of this world?"

"Paul? Nothing. Paul is an almost perfect specimen of what a man is supposed to be—kind, generous, strong, and well-informed. I think you'll like him, although I don't suppose you'll find him particularly interesting."

"Then what do you think will interest me?"

Katharine had looked surprised.

"Roxanne, his wife. I think you'll find Roxanne interesting."

Bryce had stared at her briefly. "Katharine, are you trying to get rid of me?" he joked uneasily.

She'd laughed, of course.

In the airplane, Bryce thought of all the things Katharine had explained to him before he left. "Explained," he decided, was misleading. They were conversations, as spare and ambiguous as her work often was. He thought of them all the way to New York. Somewhere over the midwest he fell asleep. He woke up in San Francisco.

Chapter Three

■

December 1—

Paul called just now. He says we're having company for dinner. Katharine Craig's companion. I can't remember his name. Used to be a cop—does something else now. Writing? Yes, I think that's what it is. Wonder why Paul invited him here? Politeness, I suppose. Paul is always so polite. Or is he suspicious? He has such a passion for cause and effect—the result of being a stockbroker. He looks at me differently nowadays. And he is not so . . . open as he used to be. I miss that, somehow. But it's also a relief.

I suppose I will have to be gracious tonight . . .

"Hello. I'm Paul Gautier."

The man held out his hand and Bryce took it. Gautier was a small man, well-dressed, and completely at home in the expensive ultra-modern surroundings of the restaurant. His face was covered with a manicured beard; his hair was dark, graying at small points at his temples. Bryce guessed the gray was premature.

"Kevin Bryce."

Paul smiled and made a gesture indicating they should sit. A waiter came almost immediately to their table and they ordered drinks.

"Is your hotel all right? I wrote Katharine you were welcome to stay with us."

"I'm fine, thank you. The hotel is very nice."

Gautier looked reassured.

"Katharine said you would prefer to stay in a hotel. She says you're a writer. Writers like to be alone, don't they? Peculiar, I think." He shook his head and smiled. "My wife likes to be alone. My wife is a painter."

"I know."

"Of course," Gautier said, and looked embarrassed.

An understanding man, Katharine had said, easy to talk to because he listens. Bryce thought this must be true since she had mentioned his writing to Gautier. It was a subject, because of its complications, she did not discuss.

"You're in town on business? I mean, of another sort?" Gautier asked him.

"Yes. I have some property on the west shore of Lake Tahoe. My real estate agent thinks he has a buyer. There are some details to work through and papers to sign." The one detail Bryce had not properly worked through was whether he really wanted to sell. The land, along with its cabin, had been his grandparents' home, and before his move with Katharine to Ireland, his too. Now it stood empty.

"Nice place, Tahoe," Gautier remarked. "We have a little house there." He fidgeted, playing with a book of matches taken from a clean ashtray, and Bryce smiled.

"Yes. More commercial now than it used to be. Katharine tells me you're a stockbroker."

"Yes. A little dull to some, maybe, but I like it." Gautier

glanced into the narrow opening of his glass. "I tried explaining stocks to Katharine one day, and nearly put her to sleep."

Bryce laughed softly, and Gautier relaxed.

"But you—you have an interest in business, don't you? Or in some of its theories?"

"I'm more interested in people than in the flow of cash," Bryce answered cautiously.

"But they can be related, can't they? Can't one be directly influenced by the other? Of course they can. You won't disagree, will you?"

"No."

"Are you familiar with art at all? I mean, other than Katharine's?"

"Somewhat."

"Are you familiar with Kirchner? The German Expressionist?"

Bryce nodded. Gautier leaned forward over the table as if in anticipation, his hands spread open.

"You've seen his paintings? Perhaps read something about him and his ideas?" Gautier went on as if confident of an affirmative answer. "Then, with this in mind, in a society ruled by exchange, especially a society as diverse and money conscious as ours, what would you classify as its fundamental transaction—in its most basic, or base, form?"

"Prostitution," Bryce said after a pause.

Gautier sat back and tapped his fingers on the table.

"May I ask what this has to do with your wife? You weren't very specific in your letter."

"Have you seen my wife's work?"

"No."

"Up until a year ago her work did well enough—interesting, I suppose, in its way. But then it took a radical departure—perhaps not so much in style as in theme." Gautier picked up his drink, then ignored it. "Color has always been a primary concern of hers. Even her blacks and whites are somehow vibrant. She often applies color thickly, in a kind of swirling brush stroke—always makes me think of the bay when it's choppy—but her subjects . . . her subjects are now prostitutes—male prostitutes—and she depicts not just death, but murder."

Bryce's eyes had been fixed into the depths of his scotch. He raised them slowly to meet those of the man across from him. Gautier couldn't sit still; using a thumb, he carefully pressed the sweat from his glass.

"What is it that concerns you, exactly?"

"Last September. . . there was a dead boy washed up on the rocks below the Golden Gate Bridge. A beautiful boy. There are a lot of kids like him in San Francisco, although most aren't as—successful—as he was. A lot of them," Paul said, absently.

"Who was he?"

"His name was Taylor Adams. He was an artist's model, among other things. My wife's model, more specifically. In her last and most successful show."

They were silent, and Bryce noticed for the first time that the music softly playing in the restaurant was an Elizabethan Christmas carol. The commercial signs of the season were all around them: white tablecloths; crimson arrangements of flowers, accented with sprigs of holly; exhausted shoppers resting in booths with hot toddys, large bags from Macy's or Neiman-Marcus or Gump's at their feet.

"What exactly do you want from me?" Bryce asked.

"Separate a few facts from a few lies, if you can."

"For what purpose?"

"My peace of mind," Gautier answered wearily, then drained half his drink. Bryce wondered what made Gautier sure separating a few facts from a few lies would guarantee him peace of mind. "I don't know what my wife might have seen—what she might know. I want her protected. I want to get her some kind of help if she needs it."

"Do you?" Bryce looked at his companion speculatively, his professional instincts aroused. "Are you more interested in what she's seen or what she's done?"

In a jerky motion Gautier spilled part of his drink, then soaked up the mess with his cocktail napkin.

"I don't know. I'm not an imaginative man. I don't know what she *could* have done."

"Was she having an affair with Taylor Adams?"

"I don't know. I'm not too sure I want to know."

Gautier made rings on the table with his glass; clusters of shoppers bustled by. The music segued to an excerpt from the Nutcracker ballet.

"What was the official ruling on Adam's death?"

"What do you mean?"

"Murder, accidental—"

"Suicide."

"But you don't believe that?"

"If I knew what to believe, I wouldn't need you."

"What makes you think you have anything to worry about?" The question was probably unanswerable. Bryce just wanted to see Gautier's response.

Gautier rubbed his face with his hands and stared at the table for a while before answering.

"The gallery where her last exhibit is displayed is on Sutter Street. Take a look at what's there and then imagine the woman you love painting them." His eyes rested on Bryce's face. "You are a writer living with another artist. Tell me, what is the source of her inspiration? I am a layman—a pragmatic, unimaginative man. Maybe I take it all too literally."

"Give me the address of the gallery. I'll take a look at the exhibit, but I'm not promising I can do any more than that."

Bryce saw Gautier's shoulders shift in relief as he took a pen and one of his cards from an inside pocket of his coat. He wrote on the back and handed it to Bryce.

"You'll come to dinner tonight?"

"Yes."

Gautier smiled gratefully. "If you could arrive between seven and seven-thirty, that would be good. I appreciate this. Katharine said you were . . . reluctant." He looked away, watching an attractive young woman walk by, a dozing child on one arm, packages balanced on the other.

"I don't want to be tied up any longer than I have to. I want to get back," Bryce explained shortly.

"I don't blame you. Heard Katharine staged quite a show in London. Love seems to have made her extraordinarily creative."

"Why? Did Katharine *say* she loved me?" Bryce's intensity startled Gautier.

"No," he stammered. "Not exactly."

Of course. She wouldn't. Not exactly.

It was dark. The windows of Macy's were lighted with fluorescent lamps hidden under mounds of artificial snow, spotlighting mechanical dolls. Dickensian women with muffs and high collars, men in top hats and coats, children wrapped in caps and scarves, moved in slow motor-propelled movements, dancing, riding in sleighs, caroling, stirring a pot at the hearth. Bryce stopped to observe them as crowds pushed past. An old woman played "Jingle Bells," badly, on a small keyboard instrument. Nearby, sitting in a wheelchair, a legless man sold pencils, his face weathered, as if it had been chipped from wood. The aroma of expensive perfume filled Bryce's nostrils, a heady scent made sharper by the cold air. Next to him stood two stylishly dressed women, one in gray silk and a red fox coat, the younger wearing cream-colored trousers and an oversized cashmere sweater the same pale shade as the pants. Her hair was dark and full, loosely pinned to the top of her head, like a Gibson girl. The smell of money was stronger than the scent of the perfume. A horn honked and the women turned. In a few quick steps they were at the curb, where a man in a brand-new Mercedes had the car door already open for them. Smiling and laughing, they got in, carelessly tossing their packages in the backseat, starting to tell the man of their day's experience.

Bryce's sense of isolation became suddenly overwhelming. He took another look at the displays, then continued up the street. At the corner were two Vietnamese children, large-eyed and boisterous, hawking garlic. Bryce bought two bags and handed each child a dollar.

A half a block from the gallery, his eye was caught by a mannequin in the display window of a boutique. It was wearing a sweater thickly knit in a soft yarn the color of ripe apricots, a series of tiny apricot silk handkerchiefs knotted into the bottom half of the weave. It looked like something Katharine would wear, and he paused in front of the window to imagine her dressed in it. The image was so powerful, he was sure that if he went in to take a closer look, the sweater would smell the way all her clothes came to smell—a soft scent of perfume that rubbed off her skin into the fabric. With a little more life to his step, he continued the last few paces to the gallery.

After an hour in the gallery, Bryce had seen everything he needed to see.

Chapter Four

■

December 1—

Overate at dinner and had to make myself throw up. Dinner was rather more than I expected, and Katharine's friend different from what I thought he might be. Must be older than her by a dozen years. I don't know why I should find that surprising—after all, it's common enough. Maybe because I heard she uses him as a model. Perhaps, too, it is the kind *of man that comes as a surprise. I suppose I expected someone more self-indulgent.*

I've always wondered what anyone sees in a writer—they're such an obnoxious breed—but he's not cut from the same anemic mold of most writers I know. He is attractive without being conventionally handsome. Looks like he's spent a lot of time outdoors with his hands in the dirt, rather than his head in the clouds.

Perhaps Katharine's choice is not so unexpected after all.

"Roxanne has very blond hair, pale clear from the roots. Wonderful bone structure in her face. Fair skin. And a dancer's body.'' Katharine had paused so long over that bust, concentrating on some small detail, that Bryce thought she was finished. Suddenly she stood straight and continued. ''An *anorexic* dancer. She also has very large green eyes. I suppose what makes them so extraordinary is the way they're set against such delicate bone structure.''

An articulate description for Katharine. He came behind her and covered her eyes with his hands.

''What color are my eyes?'' he asked.

''Hazel. But sometimes they change.'' He took his hands away. ''Didn't expect me to know, did you?'' she challenged, smug. And curious.

The address he had given the cabbie turned out to be a well-kept building in Pacific Heights where a guard in the lobby called the Gautier apartment before Bryce was allowed to enter the elevator.

Gautier himself answered the door and escorted Bryce to the living room, where much of the polished parquet floor was covered by a carpet of American Indian design—broad strips of pale blue, pinstripes of cream and pale yellow, a line of diamonds in rose—on which stood sofas of white linen. On each sofa were thrown a few pillows in beautiful colors—fuchsia, cobalt blue, forest green, bright yellow; some solid, some in stripes. On an ebony coffee table, in a silver vase that reflected the colors, was an arrangement of white and red roses, in full bloom. There were three chairs upholstered in linen: one in peach; one in carnelian blue; one in mauve, accented with a long cloth woven in threads of white and yellow. For all its colors, it was a strangely harmonic room, the kind of room reserved for friends, drinks, and good conversation. Flames licked the inside of the fireplace. Framed by the lights of the city, a Christmas tree stood before a window, smelling of pine like Tahoe, with small white flickering lights and delicate glass balls. At the far end of the room, at a carved ebony bar, Gautier served Bryce a drink while they waited for Roxanne to join them.

She entered wearing a green silk dress. It rustled with a soft, elegant sound as she walked into the room. Despite Katharine's description, the work of Roxanne Gautier had made such an indelible impression on Bryce that he had expected to see something of the whore in her appearance. Instead he was greeted by what seemed to be every inch a lady.

She moved in the simple dress with the grace of a prima ballerina. Her smile was quick and direct, disturbingly compelling. Only her hands, dried and cracked from turpentine, nails and skin discolored by paint, revealed that she was used to work.

When they were well into their small talk, a slender Eurasian girl brought in a tray with an assortment of cheese, pâté with truffles, and smoked salmon canapes. Gautier fixed Roxanne a Campari soda, and she drank it as though it tasted sweet, not bitter, seated across from Bryce, the green of her dress vivid against the white sofa.

"I understand Katharine uses you as a model," she said.

"Only in bits and pieces," Bryce replied. "A hand here, a head of hair there, nothing anyone would ever recognize as me."

"Roxanne never uses me . . . completely absent from anything she does," Gautier said, when his wife laughed. He shoved a carbon cartridge into a seltzer bottle. The water sizzled violently to the top. "Considering her subject matter, I suppose I should be grateful." He poured himself another drink.

Roxanne smiled at him over her shoulder. "So you should." She turned back to Bryce. "My husband finds some of my work shocking."

"You're not the first artist to use prostitution as your basis of communication," Bryce said with academic precision.

"You've seen the show?"

"What's left of it."

"Are you an art enthusiast, Kevin?"

"I find it interesting, like I do a lot of other things," Bryce said. "Perhaps a little more since meeting Katharine."

"Kevin was the man responsible for putting an end to those art robberies at Lake Tahoe," Gautier told her.

Roxanne looked at Bryce with more interest.

"Art robberies? I think I remember reading something..."

"Roxanne isn't much for reading newspapers or watching the six o'clock news," Gautier said wryly, coming around the bar to sit next to his wife, perching himself on the arm of the white sofa.

"Paul tries to tell me the news over dinner, but I'm afraid I have a tendency to nod off. I'm an ignoramus," she finished, looking anything but, and taking Gautier's hand.

The perfect couple, Katharine had said.

"Are you still involved with police work?" Her tone was polite.

"Sometimes," he said, then added, "but I'm no longer in any official capacity."

"I see." She smiled. "A freelance operation now?"

"I wouldn't call it that, exactly."

"A man of leisure who pursues only what interests him?"

Bryce laughed. "I suppose you could say it that way."

"Tell me, how do you know when something should be pursued or when it should be left alone?"

"I don't always."

"Then you do think there are things that should be left alone?" She eyed him with a fraction more curiosity.

"Depends on what we're talking about. If there is a crime involved, then it should be pursued. If someone is victimized, then the reasons for it should be discovered."

"So it's the motive rather than the actual crime that interests you?"

"Motives are interesting things but sometimes difficult to

discover. Completely different motives can inspire the same action and the same result—at least, on the surface."

"So they can," she said, thoughtfully considering her drink.

"Sometimes someone trying to do the least damage does the most."

She looked up at him quickly. "But a crime is a crime, no matter what the original intentions, surely?"

"Someone always suffers," Bryce responded.

Roxanne brought Paul's hand to her mouth and pressed her lips to it in an unconscious gesture with no more significance than the idle plucking of a stray thread.

"And as a policeman it was your job to see the offender was brought to justice?" she pressed, leaning forward.

"It was my job to collect data and apprehend a suspect," he corrected. "I've never been a judge or a prosecutor."

"But surely you formed an opinion?"

"I'm not a robot," Bryce said. "I just had to be careful to balance what I felt with what I did."

Roxanne sat back in her seat. "Don't we all?" she asked rhetorically.

The maid returned to announce that dinner was ready.

"Are you here on business, Kevin?" Roxanne asked, looking up from the consommé.

"I've some property in Tahoe—I've come to take care of the details of selling it."

"Oh? Is that your only business?"

"More or less."

Roxanne smiled and took her last spoonful of soup.

"Tell me, did you do all your own decorating?" Bryce asked. The clean lines of the polished ebony table almost blended into the black marbleized floor and contrasted with the white place settings; a centerpiece of pale pink roses in a light gray vase softened the black and white austerity.

She has mastered the complexities of being a hostess, Katharine had said.

"Yes," she answered.

"It's very nice. Do you have a room of your own?"

"Of my own?'"

"Someplace where you can do your work and no one can intrude without your permission."

Gautier pushed his plate back. The maid took it away.

"Yes, as a matter of fact, I do."

"You'll have to show it to him," Gautier suggested.

"Yes, I suppose I will . . . sometime."

The maid took Roxanne's plate. As she bent down to pick up Bryce's, he looked up at her and was caught off guard. The girl smiled and moved away.

As dinner ended, the maid came to tell Gautier he had a telephone call, and Gautier, apologetic, excused himself. As he left, Roxanne took Bryce by the arm and led him to a combination game room and library. It was a traditional room, solid and warm, polished wood and Oriental rugs, black leather chairs and leatherbound books. Photographs lined the walls and crowded the far corners of a mahogany desk; family photos, Paul and Roxanne in front of a sailboat. In the center of the room was a billiard table, on one wall a dart board, on a corner table a chessboard.

"This is Paul's room," Roxanne said.

"Very nice," Bryce murmured. Roxanne still did not release him, but moved her grip down to take hold of his hands. Her own were cool and dry.

"Kim will bring coffee in a minute," she said, and absently turned his hands, looking at them. "I can see why Katharine uses these."

"Can you?"

"Yes, they're very dramatic," she said thoughtfully. "Masculine. They look like they've had a rough life. Have they?"

Bryce merely shrugged, looking at her as directly as she

looked at him. She gave her attention back to his hands, turning them again, tracing one of his old scars with her thumb.

"Very impressive," she remarked.

"But not an overwhelming source of inspiration for you."

"As I said, they're impressive. But my taste tends to run in other directions," she admitted, amused, releasing his hands. "What would you care to play? Chess? Darts? Or pool?"

"Whatever you prefer."

"Pool, then," she said. From a case mounted on the wall she extracted two cues and handed one to Bryce. "Nothing serious. Just bouncing the ball around to see where it lands."

"Fine," he said, and racked the balls.

"I suppose you want me to break?" she asked.

"Ladies first."

She laughed and chalked her cue, adding streaks of blue to her already discolored fingers. Her hands, thought Bryce, were rather masculine; thick and round at the tips of her fingers, wide across the palm. Holding the cue firmly she positioned herself to shoot. She called her shots and the balls went to their designated pockets unhesitantly. One. Two. Three. Four. A simple game of rotation. She missed ball ten.

"Your shot," she told him.

"You didn't leave me much."

"I didn't intend to," she said flatly. And smiled, as an afterthought.

Bryce didn't call his shots. His first inched slowly into a side pocket, his second rolled uselessly to the far end of the table. Roxanne finished off the last four balls and then reracked them.

"You break," she ordered lightly.

He did. Balls scattered. Four dispersed themselves into different pockets. White ball made number five. Scratch.

Kim, the Eurasian maid, came in, setting up a tray with coffee while Bryce watched, noting how pretty, how feminine her movements were. Makeup accentuated the exotic features without overdramatizing them. He looked back at the pool table as Kim left, discovering that he, too, had been the subject of scrutiny.

"Would you like to see more of her while you're in town?"

"Of *her*?"

"So you've already guessed." She seemed pleased, moving around the table to improve her position for the next shot. "Very perceptive of you."

"Is he gay, too, or does he just prefer women's clothes?"

"Just likes the fancy clothes and makeup. How did you know?"

Bryce shrugged. "Hard to say. Chemistry is a peculiar thing. Let's just say," he continued whimsically, "while his appearance suggested one thing, the general signals did not tally with the appearance." He paused. "Besides, he'd smudged his makeup."

Roxanne took her shot and missed.

"Very good. It took Paul longer than it did you. Made him terribly uncomfortable for some reason. But he got used to it. Sees it all as part of the local flora. . . . That was a good shot."

"How long did it take you?"

"I knew instantly. As you say, chemistry *is* a peculiar thing. So is intuition. For example, my intuition tells me you've been throwing your shots. Now why would you throw your shots? Is it that you're being polite and don't want to beat the house? Or maybe you don't like to show off. Or could it be that you want to see how I play, lull me into complacency? If this turned into a game, would your skill suddenly improve?"

"Maybe I just don't shoot pool well," he said, stopping to chalk his cue.

"You look very capable."

"Looks can be deceiving."

"But they aren't usually. At least, not for long."

"If you know what to look for," he agreed, and took another shot doomed to limited success.

"And I do," she said, her face hardening slightly around the eyes, the fine lines at the corners of her mouth compressing into a more determined set. Bryce noticed, too, that her surface had chipped a little, like a scrap of paint on a windowsill that has bubbled and broken to reveal a vacuum.

"Obviously," he said, stepping back from his last shot to watch the ball roll into the pocket. It fell with a dull thud accentuated by a clatter of balls. "Don't be too quick to show your opponent what you do best—keep it a surprise."

She stared at him for a moment, then suddenly smiled, an expression hung precariously between social function and sincerity.

"Well, then," she said, racking the balls once more, "let's change the subject a little." And Bryce knew they weren't really going to change the subject at all. "If you're going to be modest with your talents, tell me about your failures. What about the ones who got away? The ones that couldn't be prosecuted."

Bryce paused to bounce the fat end of his stick on the floor. He had a habit of doing that, bouncing things. He did it at his desk with pencils and pens and erasers, at the dining room table with the blunt end of a knife or a fork. It gave him something to do when he wished to think or did not wish to speak right away.

"There was one case. A man in his early twenties. He had a bad habit of molesting ten-year-old girls in public parks. Sometimes he had a moustache, sometimes a beard, sometimes a black stocking over his head—he did things like that to confuse the already traumatized children when they went to identify him. He had an impressive way of introducing them to sex. He knocked out their front teeth. . . ." Out of the corner of his eye he watched Roxanne. Her face conveyed interest and a certain watchfulness, like a baseball pitcher judging a batter. "After that, the girls had little reason to doubt the other threats he made, and they cooperated as quietly as they could. We had an idea who it was. We tailed him, and finally he was caught in the act by a sheriff's deputy and eventually brought to trial."

"And?" she prompted. There was a tautness in her voice Bryce was immediately aware of, urging him not to dawdle.

"He was released on a technicality. He had well-to-do parents, a good lawyer, and good grades in school. He was popular. He was even well-liked. Why should he want to rape anyone? He was also a cocky little bastard."

"So he's still on the streets?"

Bryce stopped his tapping and looked at her.

"No, he's dead," he said shortly.

"How?"

"A short time after he was released, he had to go to the hospital. As it turned out, he needed a blood transfusion."

"Why did he need a transfusion?"

Bryce leaned his cue against the oak table. "He was found in a public park by a jogger, this time molesting a twelve-year-old. The jogger, a woman, summoned the police. In trying to escape, the man fell down two flights of concrete stairs, and at the bottom, his mouth somehow rammed into the corner of a town memorial. He was badly cut and bruised and managed to have all his teeth knocked out," Bryce explained with exquisite gentleness. It was possible Roxanne's attention took an extra edge, a fraction more sharpness. "He lost enough blood that his doctor thought it expedient they give him a transfusion. When he recovered, he was taken back on trial, and again released."

"So we're back to 'how did he die?' " she reminded him quietly.

"The blood donor, the hospital discovered later, had AIDS. The 'alleged' molester died a little over a year later."

The whole of Roxanne's dancer's body was very still.

"That was one who got away," he said softly.

Roxanne laughed. "Your arms are too short to box with God. In the second arrest, Kevin, who was the arresting officer?"

"Don't quite remember."

"I see. And whoever it was couldn't catch up with him until *after* he fell down those stairs."

"That's what my report says."

"Kevin, exactly what kind of books do you write? Would I have read any of them?"

"Probably."

"I don't remember seeing your name on any cover."

"Possibly because I write under a pseudonym."

"Which is?"

"John Steinbeck."

Roxanne sat down in a chair as if the weight of her body was suddenly too much for her and laughed heartily.

"My, my, my, hasn't Katharine gotten herself a handful," she remarked unselfconsciously. Her eyes sparkled. "What do you see in Katharine? Except for some remarkable one-liners, she is an inarticulate personality." She measured his silence. "Are you offended or just not talking?"

"Your shot," he said, and added as she positioned herself to shoot, "Maybe it's a case of opposites attracting."

The balls clacked. Three of them separated from the crowd and moved into opposing pockets.

"Nonsense. Opposites do not attract," she said with the assurance of one with access to the facts. She studied the table. "We're only attracted to someone who appears opposite when we discover something in them that is familiar—that we can identify with. The attraction is that something that on the surface seems so strange is also familiar, so much at home."

"Have you spent a lot of time studying the mechanics of attraction?"

"It's an interesting subject," she answered, sounding like someone who had long ago explored other avenues of interest and found them lacking.

"What's an interesting subject?" inquired Gautier, coming into the room.

"Your wife has just effectively refuted one of the oldest

maxims in history. She is convincing me that opposites do not attract,'' Bryce said.

Gautier gave a weary wave of his hand. ''I've heard the theory before, and I don't completely agree, although I think it may be true for some people. I've just never been able to decide if those people are extraordinarily narcissistic or perversely sympathetic.''

''Your shot, Kevin,'' she said. ''Personally, I vote for narcissism. What about you?''

One by one, Bryce shot each ball into the pockets in a practiced, harmonic rhythm. Afterward he stopped to regard the empty table with what appeared to be a lack of satisfaction.

''I prefer to reserve judgment,'' he said, friendly if regretful at disappointing his hostess. He replaced his stick in the case and glanced at his watch. ''It's getting late. I should be going. Thank you for dinner. It was a treat, being away from home, like this.''

Gautier posed the usual objections, but Kevin was politely adamant. Roxanne stood by silently, and with the expertise of the socially practiced, did so without being rude.

''Well, then,'' said Gautier, giving in gracefully, ''I'll get your coat and call a cab.''

''Good luck. You might have a hell of a wait. The traffic out there is *miserable*.''

They all turned. A man stood at the door, the upper half of his body obscured by the pyramid of packages balanced on his arms.

''My God,'' said Gautier, rushing to rescue a package squeezing out from the middle of the heap. ''A little early, aren't you, Santa?''

As each package was removed, piled slowly on the billiard green, a bit more of this new arrival was revealed. He was short and round, as if, though in his twenties, still waiting to lose his baby fat. Dark-haired and fair-skinned, like Gautier, but without the sharp handsomeness of his features, it seemed the young man could be attractive or ugly, as though time had not yet defined what form he would take.

The newcomer shed a pair of leather gloves as he explained:

"Mother is keeping Peggy's pathetic little brats for the rest of the week, and she wanted to make sure these were safe from prying fingers. I think she's leaving them with you rather than me because she doesn't trust me not to open them. Hello." He put out his hand to Bryce.

"Kevin, this is my brother Rob," said Gautier. "Rob, Kevin Bryce."

The two men shook hands, then Rob turned back to his brother.

"Is it true you're going out of town tomorrow?"

"Yes, I'll be gone for a couple of days."

"Lucky you. Can I have some of that coffee over there with a little cognac in it? It's *cold* outside." He slapped his hands against his arms.

"I'll get it for you," Roxanne said.

Bryce saw Rob pause, the movement of his hands, just briefly, stalled.

"Oh, why not let the pope get it for me? Don't bother yourself," he said, and Roxanne stayed where she was, making a small, almost fatalistic gesture. Paul moved slowly to pour the coffee, adding the cognac while Rob, in answer to Bryce's questioning look, explained: "A nickname, Pope Paul the Good versus Robin the little hood." He appeared to relish this difference.

Paul handed Rob his drink with a dry but tolerant: "There's some silliness Rob has never outgrown."

"To never growing up," Rob said, raising his glass.

Bryce smiled and said: "I really ought to be going."

It was Roxanne, alone, who eventually walked Bryce to the living room. There, in the flickering light of the Christmas tree, they peered through the brightly decorated branches for the cab while Paul attended to another call.

"Does he always get so many phone calls?" Bryce asked.

"Depends on the state of the market. A lot of clients consider themselves friends and therefore entitled to call at any hour. Also, Paul comes from a large close-knit family. Sometimes I think San Francisco must have had to put up extra phone lines just for the Gautiers.'' Bryce laughed softly, and so did Roxanne. ''Do you have much family, Kevin?''

''No.''

''Neither do I. And I like it that way. No muss, no fuss, and no irrelevant advice,'' she catalogued good-naturedly.

''Was there a fuss with Rob at one time?''

She frowned. ''He used to like me—I honestly don't know what happened.'' She shrugged and smiled. ''Ah, well, it makes the conclusion unanimous.''

''Happy on your island?'' he asked.

She looked up at him, mocking. ''We're not in this world to be happy. We're here to be productive.''

''Then most of us fail.''

''But not you, Kevin. I imagine you're very productive.'' When she looked at him now, her eyes were like a cat's, able to see in the dark, straightforward yet revealing nothing. Bryce became still, the way he had taught himself to become when he was wary, when he needed to keep his head. ''My husband,'' she said, ''is an open book. But a very good book, don't you think? Like *Moby Dick*. Or maybe something by Trollope. Maybe I'm overly suspicious, but I don't think you're here just to sign a few documents.''

''Are you telling me you have a guilty conscience?''

''What I'm telling you is that you'll never be able to prosecute me.''

Bryce folded his arms and stared at her, unable to decide if this was an obscene declaration of criminal vanity or a serious statement of fact.

''There's no court of law in this world that could convict me.''

Bryce looked past her.

''My cab is here,'' he said. ''If Paul is leaving town tomorrow, why don't you let me take you out to dinner?''

"Katharine won't object?"

Why should she? he thought. Wasn't she the one who set me up for this thing? Sent me on a silver platter? But he said: "No, I don't think so. Not at all." He paused, but she remained silent. "Shall I pick you up at seven or at eight?"

"Eight," she said, and sighed. "Eight o'clock will be fine. But avoid taking me anyplace with stairs, will you?"

CHAPTER FIVE

■

Trying to trace the source of things can be so difficult. I wonder why I feel so compelled to do it. I don't like dwelling on the past. But I can't stop thinking. Somehow I imagine if I write it out I will . . . what? Be absolved? But that's too absurd to contemplate. There is no absolution. There is no mercy.

What I remember first is the joy of doing something I shouldn't. I feel elated, sitting in the middle of the floor; sunshine, warm and direct, spills through the window. I'm in my mother's special room. It has a piano, a small gray couch, a table with books and tidbits of all her half-finished hobbies. An embroidery of a horse tight in its hoop, the tail and background unfinished, sheets of music spread on the piano, a red book open, facedown on the couch—I think it is Emile Zola's Nana, *because that was the only red book I found in Mother's collection some years later. In the corner sat a canvas on which was painted an unfinished nude, consisting mainly of a woman's back. Scattered next to it were turpentine, brushes, tubes of paint. She must have stopped painting not long before and carelessly left one tube open. It drooled a bright blue. Tentatively, drawing my hand back quickly at its moistness, I touched, pleased with the thick, oily softness as I rubbed my thumb and forefinger together. The smell was strong. I took as many tubes as my two small hands could hold, and sat on the hard floor in the sunshine, uncapped them and squeezed. I remember the colors; yellow, violet, blue, red. I remember the way they shot into the air like fireworks; I remember their weight and thickness, the way I could squeeze a rainbow of color through my small fingers and smear a design of swirling motion on my arm. It absorbed my heat, felt warm and sticky on my neck. Thick, I had to have it thick, to color my body like a book with crayons. I felt contented as only a child can when she sees something beautiful.*

I step outside myself and see me as my mother must have when she walked into the room. A small, blond three-year-old baking herself in the sun, surrounded by a pool of paint. Oiled from head to toe, it matted her hair and streaked over a new yellow playsuit. She smiles and opens wide her hand, displaying a sticky, colorful palm.

Such was the initiation into my love affair with paint. It's here I learned the drying effect of turpentine; that pain is often the aftermath of pleasure.

Next I remember standing in the hall to one side, out of the light. I feel small but I am now older than three. I see my mother, a man on one side, a woman on the other. They are holding her arms. She spits, she screams. But still they lead her forward. She disowns me, hurls filthy abuse at my father. And still they lead her forward. Our hall is long. It becomes longer still. It seems never-ending.

I don't see my mother again for a long time. When I do, it's in a hospital. Yellow light diffused through white curtains, the smell of lemon-scented antiseptic. My mother's eyes, dark blue and earnest; she explains to me about Jack, who lives under her bed and every night climbs the beanstalk sprouted from her mattress. She whispers the details in my ear, afraid of eavesdroppers.

I was an effective keeper of her secrets mainly because I failed to remember them. I visit her often and should know every bizarre anecdote by heart. But they are painful to listen to.

I remember when she was beautiful. I vaguely remember that there were times when Mother was always touching, always stroking, always kissing. Maybe a person's capability for ugliness can only be measured by their capability for beauty. I don't know. It seemed to be doled out to her in equal measure, but somewhere along the line the darkness broke the dike and flooded the light.

At first I am frightened. Then I am sickened. Eventually I begin to accept insanity as a part of life, take violence for granted.

For many years I see her regularly. Cautiously I explore my mind to find what I felt then, and can scarcely believe it. Why is it children are born with such a sense of responsibility? Because I love her I feel I must help her, that I can make a difference. In books isn't it often the loving child who is the savior?

But I am no savior.

As I grow older there are occasional excursions together into the outside world; rare lunches, an afternoon of shopping. I remember nothing of these except having to mollify the waitresses, the salespeople she would offend.

"I'm sorry, she's not well, please excuse her..." I smile. I leave a large tip.

Every visit becomes more painful and twisted than the last. It is here I become infuriated by failure, that I learn the futility of trying to make a difference in someone's life. I insulate myself by thinking of color, of form, of fine details that could be used for emphasis. My brush rarely fails, and there is security in its mastery. I become the object of praise.

These sessions become useful.

* * *

My father spent so much energy on my mother he had little left for me. That I can understand. I don't understand why he would look at me and turn away. I don't understand why he would acknowledge me with a cursory pat on the head, like I was a convenient dog. I don't understand why at sixteen he gave me a car. And I don't understand why, when I drove out the driveway for the last time two years later, there were tears in his eyes.

Chapter Six

■

December 2—

God, what a day so far! Terrible breakfast. Eggs—they're such slimy, nasty things. I couldn't eat any of them. Gave Kim the day off and had to fix my own lunch—cottage cheese with raisins. Interesting color and texture once you've mushed it around. So interesting I forgot to eat it.

I did not, however, forget to go to the newspaper. It took me a while to search through those back issues of the Chronicle, *but it was worth it. What was more enlightening was Laura. There's a lot of truth that never reaches print, just as there's a lot of lies that do. But Laura is usually accurate. And, of course, she was on the spot.*

Kevin Bryce. A man who spends two years chasing a thief, and then, when it's all said and done, leaves the country with the poor bastard's widow.

Maybe he is my kind of man, after all.

After I left Laura's office, I went to the gallery. I haven't been there for a while. In the beginning I went all the time, just so I could relive that heady sense of accomplishment, reassure myself that I had succeeded at what I tried to do. Maybe I still feel that way, though less intensely. What I did, I did well.

I usually do.

I couldn't help thinking of Taylor. In my paintings his face is not as beautiful as it was in life. But I did capture the innocence. That was what was so astonishing about him. That he had been in the business so long and could still conjure that clear-eyed, unspoiled look. No one could figure it. But it was faith, of course. The substance of things hoped for, the evidence of things not seen, as the Bible says. Faith in what? I don't know. Perhaps that he was one of those chosen to rise above circumstances, that he could be healed. Poor boy, didn't you know that the price of friendship is often higher than you want to pay?

"Kevin? Kevin Bryce? I can't believe it! Is it really you? I thought you'd taken off for parts unknown. Here, come into my office."

On the wave of this enthusiastic greeting, Bryce was ushered into the office of Angelo Grey of the SFPD. Angelo was a small wiry man, with strong Latino features inherited from his mother and a clipped, rapid form of speech learned from years of being at a disadvantage. Short, small, and gay to boot. Though he was nearing fifty, his hair was as thick and black as it had been when he was twenty. "I thought my secretary was doing his usual fucking up when he said you were waiting in the hall."

Bryce smiled, seating himself in a chair across from Angelo, who propped his scant rear end on the corner of the desk.

"How have you been?" Bryce asked.

"Good, real good. In San Francisco about four years now. So far, so good. Looks like you're doing pretty good yourself." He took a cigarette off the desk and lit it. "Leaving your job to take off to foreign countries with younger women must agree with you."

Inwardly, Bryce winced, though he supposed the description was accurate enough. "You should try it sometime."

Angelo laughed. "Not me. Get myself a good-looking eighteen-year-old boy and hock him off a street corner. Make myself a fortune in this town, and then I'll take him and run off to Arizona, where they don't have all this fucking *fog*."

"I would have thought you found paradise here," Bryce said mildly.

"There's trouble in paradise. Too many weird diseases with no cures," Angelo said, thoughtfully blowing out a lungful of smoke. "So what brings you to San Francisco? You and your lady on a little vaçation? Or did you come all this way to sit in Angelo's stinking office on Bryant Street to see how the old faggot's doing?"

"I'm here for a few days on business."

Angelo gave Bryce attention of a different sort.

"I thought you retired. Boy Wonder says hasta la-bye-bye to service twenty years before anyone expects him to."

"I did."

"So what are you doing now? Did you go private?"

"Just doing a favor for a friend. It's kind of a family matter."

"Family matter. Didn't anyone teach you to stay out of family matters? A smart boy like you? Let the family figure out their own matters."

"It's a simple affair," Bryce said, knowing this was the most extraordinary lie he had told since leaving the sheriff's department.

"If it's simple, how come you need me?"

"For information, that's all. Just information."

Angelo sighed and stubbed out his cigarette. "No chasing bandits down dark alleys? No busting into people's bedrooms while they make wild passionate whoopee? No leaping over tall buildings in a single bound?"

"No, I'm sorry. Just a look in your files."

"Kevin, you disappoint me. You haven't gone from Boy Wonder to middle-aged kaput, have you?"

"It wouldn't surprise me."

"Ha. It would me. Okay. What do you want to know? Uncle Angelo tells all," he said with a wave of his hand that ended in his lighting another cigarette.

"A few months ago there was an apparent suicide. The victim's name was Taylor Adams—"

"You asking about *Taylor*? What kind of family matter *is* this?"

"You knew him?"

"Knew him? On Polk Street Taylor was a legend in his own time. Screw anything—man, woman, stud service for the family dog—all for a fee that went up instead of down. He wasn't no kid anymore, you know. Not for that business. Jeez, but what a beauty," he mused with almost misty-eyed admiration, waving his cigarette for emphasis. "Black hair, blue eyes, and cheekbones that would make a model weep with envy. Not to mention a body everyone wanted a piece of."

"What made him so special? San Francisco is full of beautiful young men, isn't it?"

"The percentage of beautiful young men is overrated, in my opinion. But you're right—there's a fair amount to go around. But when you start considering the number that aren't a little prissy, the figures go down. And when you consider the ones that come on like your old-time heroes, the percentage goes down again. Everybody loves it. Men, women, kids, dogs, you name it.

"Besides," Angelo continued, as if astonished at the enormity of the subject, "what made Marlene Dietrich or Marilyn Monroe any different from your beautiful kid sister who marries a mechanic and moves to Peoria? Don't ask me. Some have an aloofness the rest of us poor peasants admire, and the others have a bent for self-destruction that makes us want to save them because they're beautiful and we're not. That's how they get our attention. We think of what we could do if we had what they got.

We think somehow we'll get a piece of it. This kid Taylor, maybe he had a little of both.''

''Did he ever do any legitimate modeling?''

''Some. Used to pick up an extra couple of bucks modeling for the Academy of Art. But always went back to the street. Been there all his life. God only knows when Taylor started turning tricks. Probably was one of those kids sexually abused at home. By the time they reach a certain age, they feel all they're good for is a screw. For some of them, that's about right.''

''So where or with whom did he live?''

''Good question. Taylor had more addresses in a month than most people have in a lifetime. Apartments by himself, apartments for the night, shared 'residences' with other boys, and all the clients who thought they found Nirvana and wanted to give him a home for life. He had that, you know. People thought they could love him. Wanted to save him. He never stayed anywhere for long. He and his famous collection were off and—''

''What famous collection?''

Angelo delivered him a look of mock astonishment. ''You're asking about Taylor and you don't know about his collection? I thought that was probably what this whole thing was about. Okay. I'll tell you. Only what I hear. I haven't seen, because after he died we didn't find it. But the story goes he collected pictures.''

''What kind of pictures?''

''You know. Photographs.''

Bryce looked at his companion with more deliberate attention.

''But don't get me wrong. Not the vice-squad type of thing. Just regular photographs of regular people doing regular things. You know, tourist stuff. Family photos, although as far as anybody knows, Taylor didn't have any family. He'd borrow other people's. And girls. Snapshots of pretty girls. Had a suitcase full. Some say two suitcases full. Maybe a whole warehouse.''

''But you didn't find them?''

Angelo threw up his hands as if he felt he were the victim of an unjust rebuke.

"Hey, I tell you. This kid is like one of those Arabs, moving from place to place, leaving bits of himself behind. A pair of shorts, a clock radio. Though his last year on the streets, his pattern was more peculiar."

"In what way?"

"You want to know? I'll tell you. These boys—they show up everyday—they make a living, then disappear for a few days, maybe a week or two. They find a lover who wants to take them to Hawaii or Santa Barbara or wherever and is willing to pay their way. But they always come back on the street again. Business as usual. But Taylor wouldn't show up for weeks, then he'd come around for a short binge and then—gone again. Rumor had it Taylor found someone—man, woman, or child—he could stay with for more than a week and who could afford to keep him."

"And Taylor wasn't talking?"

"Taylor did all kinds of talking. Problem was, it was all different stories. Nobody ever knew what or what not to believe. Taylor was a good storyteller."

Bryce sat up straight and leaned forward. Taking a pencil from Angelo's desk, he tapped the eraser against the desktop.

"Of course," Angelo told him, "there were all kinds of stories after some art exhibit opened. You know about the exhibit?" Bryce nodded. "None of those boys know a horse's ass about art, but some of their clients do. Word got around. They're all saying Taylor's hit it big, and the next thing they know, he's dead."

"What kind of stories?"

"All kinds. You want some specific stories you'll have to get someone else. I'm getting old. I don't listen so good to gossip anymore, and I prefer the old and stable to the young and reckless."

"Do you know if he had any friends? Could you set me up with someone?"

Angelo paused, pursing his lips to show he disapproved. "Yeah. Sure. Anything you want. This afternoon, maybe?"

"That would be good. Perfect."

"I'll leave a message at your hotel. You don't want to meet him there, do you? Break the receptionist's heart."

"It doesn't matter."

"Where are you staying?"

Bryce took a slip of paper from Angelo's desk, wrote his hotel and room number on it, and pushed the paper toward him.

"Okay. Uncle Angelo will take care of it all."

"Thanks."

"No problem. There's only one thing. Taylor was no 'apparent' suicide. He was a definite suicide. There were witnesses. Little bugger took off his brand-new pristine-white Ralph Lauren jacket, folded it neatly and left it on the bottom rail of the second tower of the Golden Gate Bridge. Then he climbed over and dove that perfect body into the water. D.O.A."

Bryce sat back and studied Angelo critically.

"You're sure?"

"Sure? Of course. What am I? An idiot like that fucking secretary out there? Like I said, there were witnesses. Two little Filipino guys who cruise the bridge in a Cushman cart—some kind of janitors. And two others. Can't remember who. I can look it up for you."

"Good. Listen, were there any foreign substances in his body? Drugs? Alcohol?"

"Don't think so. Absolutely clean, if I remember right."

"Any suicide note with the jacket?"

"No note or anything else. No wallet, no watch. Not even a penny in his pocket. If I hadn't been passing through the morgue, he might have sat there for days. Then again, maybe not. Like I said, Taylor was a legend."

"Unusual," Bryce said, thinking of Taylor's lack of personal effects.

"So it was," Angelo conceded, and managed to make it sound like an epitaph. Bryce stood. "Listen, I'll call you later. If you're not in, I'll leave a message."

"I appreciate this, Angelo. Thanks," Bryce said, holding out his hand. Angelo took it, giving it a dry squeeze.

"No problem. What else can I do? If it hadn't been for you, I would have been lynched four years ago instead of enjoying paradise, like I am." He laughed as if it were a particularly good joke. "Next time you're in the city, bring your lady. I'll take you both out and show you the time of your life. She's got to be gorgeous, huh? You don't leave the country for a dog. Not a smart boy like you."

At a little before noon Bryce sat in the spare but gracious office of Petter Swenson, listening to a man (not Petter) who was given to monologues as opposed to conversations, who was almost obscenely white and smooth, as if like a baby he had been dusted with talc every morning, head to toe. Kevin rubbed the tip of his tongue against the back of his teeth and counted the thin planks of wood set in Petter's polished oak floor.

". . . and, of course, we'll have to modernize."

"Modernize?" Bryce's head snapped up. Petter sat back in his chair, a swivel type that bobbed him up and down, and looked as blond and stoic during this assault as he did during all the other occasions of his life.

"Yes, the cabin. Couldn't set up a guest in it as it is. That shower's damn awkward. And it needs a dishwasher. There's no heat other than the fireplace. Too many bookshelves, have to get rid of some of them, of course. Then there's the jacuzzi we're going to set up when we tear down the back porch . . ."

Bryce relieved his mounting tension by uttering a quiet blasphemy that neither Petter nor his companion apparently noticed.

Why should he care what happened to it? Whole area was going to pot, wasn't it? Suburbia in the Sierras, eventually. It was just a building and a few acres of land. Still, the idea of this long-winded, jacuzzi-tossed lump of flesh neutering his old home was infuriating. Get rid of the bookshelves? The man was an ass. Bryce cut him short. Thanking him. Telling him he would consider his offer, he aggressively ushered the man out of Petter's own door. After which Bryce sat back in his chair and felt, momentarily, better. Petter endured it all with his usual lack of expression.

"Is he our only offer?" Bryce finally asked.

"No," Petter said. His voice still held a trace of his Scandinavian homeland. "There's a young man. I suspect he made his money in something unhealthy."

"God."

Petter leaned forward. "I apologize. I did not know you were so particular about your prospective buyers."

Bryce sighed. "I'm sorry, Petter. I didn't mean to waste your time."

"It was not an accusation, only an observation." Petter contemplated his desk calendar for a few seconds. "It is good property. You could hold on to it."

But somehow that suggestion was as dismal as the alternative. Hold on to it for what? Would he ever go back there to live? Not likely. And Katharine? No way.

"Let me think about it. Can I look over the other offers?"

"Of course. Take them now. Think for a day or two," Petter said. "It is not my wish to rush you. How long do you plan to stay?"

"My reservations are until Friday, but I may stay longer."

"Good. If you are not too busy, perhaps we can plan to spend an evening together. Go to the symphony." Petter made this proposal with the same objectivity he used in his business propositions. Bryce wondered if that was the only mode of expression Petter had left since his wife died, or if he had a woman or friend somewhere who made him laugh. God knows, he looked like he could use one. "I have tickets for Thursday. It's Vaughn-Williams."

"I'd enjoy that."

"Anything you need while you're in town, let me know," Petter elaborated with less stiffness. "I would be happy to help."

"Maybe there is something you can help me with. Do you know the Gautiers? Paul and Roxanne?"

"A little," he said. "We have met at parties. He is nice, so is she—exceptionally charming. But I do not care for her paintings."

"She's very talented."

"Yes, but her paintings are not what I would wish to hang in my living room—not good for the turn of the conversation, not good for the digestion, I think," he said, relaxing back into the chair and turning one corner of his mouth faintly.

"Possibly not," Bryce agreed wryly. "Do you know anything about their backgrounds?"

"No," Petter said. "Is it important that you know?"

"Yes."

"Then you should see Laura. She knows them. She writes a column for the newspaper now. She was very well-informed before. Now there is no limit to her knowledge. And she would be happy to see you, I think."

"Do you have her number?"

Petter leaned forward and flipped around the cards attached to a gold roller.

"Here it is," he said. "Home and work. It is easier to get ahold of her at work," he finished, giving Bryce the impression it was a number he called often, despite the fact he reached for the roller.

"Would it be all right if I used your phone?"

"Be my guest," he said, getting up discreetly and wandering out of his office door to confer with his secretary. In a matter of seconds the voice of Laura Parnismus rang sweetly in Bryce's ear.

"Kevin, darling. There you are! I've been sitting on pins and needles waiting for you to call."

"You have?"

"I have. Sincerely. I was sure you'd call, and I hate to be wrong. You want to pick my brains, don't you?"

"Yes, I do," he said, surprised, and wondering if Petter wasn't right, if there were no limits to Laura's knowledge.

"Thought so," she said, triumphant. "Would you like to buy me a drink? And maybe a few hors d'oeuvres? Can't have my brains unless you ply them with liquor and feed them first."

"I'd be delighted," he said.

"I thought you would. I have a table at a restaurant in the Galleria. It's the place with all those Renaissance murals on the wall. You know which one?"

"Yes."

"Five o'clock. Is that too late? Too early?" For the first time, an anxiousness touched her confident voice.

"No, perfect. Five o'clock in the Galleria."

"Lovely," she said, and hung up.

Bryce held the receiver, inspecting it critically, as if he suspected it of some kind of betrayal. Petter came back.

"It seems Laura was expecting me. She had everything arranged."

"Laura is very good at arranging things," Petter said seriously, looking as if he were well-acquainted with Laura and her arrangements. "Thursday night. Vaughn-Williams. Don't forget."

Bryce promised he wouldn't.

Chapter Seven

■

Back at his hotel Bryce found Angelo had done what was requested of him with his usual swiftness. There was a message from him to meet a young man by the name of Reno. The address, a small grocery store on the fringes of the Tenderloin. The time designated: three o'clock. At the bottom Angelo had scribbled in a tight scrawl this crude advice: "These boys lie a lot, but I don't need to tell you that—also, whatever you do, don't bend over!"

Bryce grinned and shoved the paper into his pocket. He caught a cable car and took it to California and Polk streets, where he got off and walked the final blocks to his meeting.

At that time of day the street appeared almost as ordinary as any street in any city; a mix of business people, shoppers, fast food, neighborhood shops and restaurants crowded the sidewalks. Only when you looked close did you note the difference. Bookstores had an inordinate amount of Hollywood paraphernalia on old glamour stars. Gay literature was well-stocked. Stores carried slightly off-beat clothes, gifts with just a touch of the bizarre, and the leathershops had suggestive displays. The faces that stared out from the tinted barroom windows were somehow foreign. There were an unusual number of teenagers, mostly male, and Bryce knew that more would collect as the day wore on, as it became night. They would cluster on street corners, loiter around storefronts, wander in and out of bars. Leave and return. Derive their energy from drugs and lose themselves in video games while an array of older men and punks and God only knew what else paraded past.

The grocery store was near Civic Center. Small and not well-lighted, it carried little more than liquor, candy, and a few loaves of bread. Two sad-looking video games sat in a corner surrounded by a tight circle of admirers.

Bryce stood to one side and watched for a few minutes, pondering which of these boys might be Reno. Or if Reno had been sidetracked by something more profitable, or simply decided not to show. Two of the young men were momentarily distracted by the entrance of a young girl in tight jeans and a short sweater. They jabbed one another with their elbows and made comments Bryce couldn't hear. The others gave the game their rapt attention; except one. Taller than his companions, more obviously streetwise, he watched Bryce out of the corner of his eye. The boy had detached himself from the others and was beginning to move in his direction when Bryce felt someone beside him.

"Are you Kevin?" This boy was about seventeen. His body had the meatlessness of youth, smooth-faced except for a few coarse hairs on his chin, above his lip. His eyes were blue, accented by heavy eyebrows that, like his hair, were dark.

"Are you Reno?"

"You got it, babe. Reno it is. You're the dude Angie was telling me about? Well, how do you like that? You don't look like no cop"—at the word cop, the tall youth who had been approaching stepped back and leaned against a pillar, as if that had been his intention all along—"no sir, you look too rich for that."

Bryce smiled. "I'm not a cop. Not anymore."

"I guess. That's what Angie said anyway. You wanna get out of here?" he asked, jerking his head in the direction of the door. Once outside, he turned up the collar of his canvas jacket against a sudden wind. He squinted up at the cloudy sky. "Where to now?"

"We're only a couple of blocks from Civic Center. Let's take a walk in the park."

"Okay, man. Whatever you say. A walk in the park," Reno mimicked as he began to move in that direction. "Angie says you want to talk about Taylor."

"That's right."

"You a friend of Taylor's?"

"Never met him."

"Oh, yeah?" Bryce caught the note of disbelief, disguised by the young man's natural cheerfulness. "You just a nosy son of a bitch or what?"

Bryce thought of all the possible explanations he could give and discarded them all. He simply didn't answer.

"You don't talk a lot, do you?"

"Not really."

"I do. Drove my mom crazy when I was at home," Reno said with a short laugh. "Jeez, dude, it's cold out here. Don't you feel the cold? You don't talk and you don't get cold. What do you do?"

"I'll buy you a cup of coffee," Bryce said, and did so just outside the park where a man was selling hot dogs from a cart. Reno took six packets of sugar and one by one emptied them into his cup as they sat on a bench across from the fountain. The park was deserted except for a derelict hunched into a tight ball on the grass.

"Don't talk, don't get cold, just wanna ask questions," Reno singsonged. Bryce had an idea of what was coming next, and in preparation he gently set his coffee cup on the thin slat of the bench, balancing it so it wouldn't fall. "We're talking boring, dude, really boring."

The boy took hold of Bryce's upper thigh and gave it a squeeze before he felt his wrist jerk and his arm, from the elbow down, snap behind his back at an awkward angle. He started to cry out and ended up gasping. His other arm, weakened by surprise and pain, swung uselessly to one side before grasping the bench for support.

"Talk. That's all I want," Bryce said apologetically. He shoved the arm up slightly higher.

"Yeah, man, whatever you say," the boy gasped, swallowing great gulps of air like a drowning man. "Jeez, dude, you're gonna *break my arm*! I *understand*, for Chrissake!"

Bryce released him. "Good," he said.

"Jeez, dude, I was just playing. Wanted to see where you were coming from. Just making a living. Can't blame me for trying."

"Then you can't blame me for breaking your arm," Bryce countered mildly, and picked up his cup.

Reno soothed his arm by rubbing it. "I thought if you were going to give me fifty bucks for just talking..." The boy shrugged. "Angie said you were gonna give me fifty bucks, you know."

"Angie," Bryce said, "said no such thing."

"Well, he said I was gonna get something." He laughed. The boy's good humor, Bryce reflected, seemed unshakable.

"You will."

"Jeez." The boy sat back on the bench, looping his elbows on the back of it. "Angie said I shouldn't fuck around with you. No bullshit. Angie's a cool dude—for a cop. For a faggot," he said, smacking his lips as if under his cheeriness was hidden a certain amount of disdain. Which there probably was, Bryce knew. It was an attitude he had run up against before, a peculiar double standard. Under the toughness or sweetness or whatever attitude these kids would adopt with a customer, was the idea they somehow maintained a kind of superiority over them. That no matter how many acts they performed with how many men, they couldn't be classified as a faggot. Sometimes they would go through as many women as they could to prove their point. But, for most, relationships with women would become sketchy and, finally, nonexistent. Whether they were gay or not was not a matter of particular interest to Bryce. But the pose of superiority was interesting. His father had always taught him that you were never any better than what you slept with. Perhaps for that reason he had always been careful in his own selections. That, he knew now, had been his father's intentions. But Bryce had found that attitude was not universal, least of all among the children of the street. Like everyone else, they had their own petty prejudices.

"If you're not a cop, then what are you?"

"Does it matter?"

Reno appeared to seriously think this over while drinking his coffee.

"I'll tell you one thing you are. You're pretty fast—for an old son of a bitch. Pretty damn strong," he said, grinning, giving his arm another quick rub. "Never could take any of that pain stuff. Taylor, now, Taylor could take pain. Wouldn't even flinch. Did a lot of that slave and master bullshit, you know? Not *this* kid. I don't like to hurt."

"Did you know Taylor for a long time?"

"Long enough. We were friends, y'know? Good dude, Taylor. Getting old for what he was doing. But still popular, y'know? Staying power, that's what he had. Staying power," he repeated admiringly. "What do you want to know about him?"

"Everything you do, and anything you've ever heard."

The boy whistled through his teeth, then threw his head back and laughed, displaying wide-spaced teeth stained with nicotine.

"You don't want much, do you?"

"Start with his family."

"Family. Let's see. Fucked up, what else is new? Mother is in

Monterey. Big, fat pig of a dike. Not many people know that," Reno stated with a trace of pride. "He used to go down to see her once a year to remind himself just how much he hated her."

"Father?"

"Never talked about him. Closed subject. Funny thing is, he lived with his father—not his mother—most of the time, until he hit the streets. But he would never talk about him. His mother—sometimes he would talk about her. Say she was rich or say she was poor or some kind of crazy or the most beautiful girl in the world. Those were just stories. He liked to tell stories. She *was* a dike, though. I saw her once. Me and Taylor were walking down the street and ran right into her coming out of a bar. Jeez, she was *huge*. And ugly. Not like Taylor. Taylor looked like a movie star. Liked to wear the shades. *Expensive* shades." Reno paused; Bryce waited patiently. "They just kinda looked at one another. I thought she was going to grab him, you know? Give him a hug or something. But then they went in opposite directions. Later on Taylor says, 'You see that bitch? That was my mother.' " Reno shrugged. "Weird, you know? But we're all a little strange down here."

"Did he have any brothers or sisters?"

"Halves. A half sister. Saw a picture of her. Nice piece, I tell you."

"Never met her?"

"No. She lives in the south somewhere. Sometimes they'd talk on the phone. And, boy, did he tell her tall tales. *Jeez*! I think she thought he was a stockbroker or something."

"Any girlfriends?"

"Sure—zillions of them."

"Anyone special?"

The boy ran a finger over the small sprouts above his lip. "Usually a coupla fucks and he was gone, y'know? But something was going on. He'd be gone for weeks, wouldn't even call me."

"No explanation?"

"Oh, he told stories. But I didn't believe most of them. Wound up they were a lot like the plot of the last movie he'd seen. He loved movies. Went all the time. Things with heroes in them. Those were his favorites. Sometimes he said he'd been picked up by some rich broad and taken to Hawaii or Tahoe for a couple of weeks. Or some guy to Palm Springs. Or sailing. He said that a few times. Sailing with some dude. And he'd model for this bunch of artists. He liked that a lot. Taking off his clothes and having people look at him. But then, he had something to show. Said there was some bitch there chasing him. Some dark brunette with big tits. He didn't like them like that, y'know. He liked them small and—"

"Reno, you're lying to me," Bryce said, bored with this ritual.

"I'm not lying, really, he liked—"

"About the artists he posed for. You're lying"

The boy wet his lips with his coffee-stained tongue. "What did Angie do? Set me up with God Almighty?"

"Listen, I don't have a lot of time to waste."

"Okay, okay. There was someone. I don't know her name. He'd make up all these stories, but there was one—some woman. I think she must have had a lot of money, because they went some pretty expensive places together. Taylor used to spend his own money on her, too, sometimes. He could be a real shit to girls, you know? A real shit. But I think he was good to this one. And when he was nice, the whole world lit up, you know? It was beautiful," he said, shaking his head. "He knew a good investment when he saw one. Classy, he said. Like Garbo. Whoever that is. From the way he talked—when he did talk—this one had to have been a cross between the perfect mom and the Virgin Mary. Nobody, I told him, is that perfect." He said it as though still exasperated, still trying to reason with Taylor's ghost. *Still jealous even now, are we, Reno*? "But Taylor had these ideas, I think. Things"—the boy hesitated, searching for the appropriate euphemism—"*bothered* him, you know. And he was getting old.

He wasn't going to be able to do what he was doing and have anybody wanting to *pay* him for it. They want fresh meat, you know?''

''So?''

''He was thinking, that's all. Changing. You see, in a way it's easy to get used to the streets. I mean, look, none of us have a regular job—not for long. Why should we? We can make a fucking fortune out here. But,'' he said with a nervous enthusiasm, ''we spend it too. Coke and heroin and video games. Booze. Clothes. I mean it gets *blown*, dude. And the hours are crazy, and parties—God, the parties. Makes it kinda hard to settle down, you know? Gets in your blood. You gotta have something to keep you going all the time. Taylor wanted something else, but he was hooked. Life here makes everything else so boring. But he was running out of time. You can't do this shit forever. You gotta take care of yourself,'' he declared. It suddenly occurred to Bryce that Reno, though out of control, was intelligent. He probably took good care of Taylor—as much as Taylor would let him. ''This last year, Taylor was thinking more. I don't know what he had in mind exactly—maybe he didn't know either. But he had something cooking in the back of his head. Maybe he thought he could make a living being a model. If that was it, I was all for it.'' It must have been hard for Reno, Bryce thought, trying to balance his natural goodwill and his jealousy. ''Maybe he could even get into the movies or something.''

''But?''

''I wasn't sure. I didn't know. But I think he might have had other ideas. Just the way he talked—or maybe the way he wouldn't talk. And I didn't trust her. What's she gonna do with Taylor? A woman like that? Take him out, introduce him to her *friends*? And Taylor—to hear him talk, you'd never think he'd ever given a blowjob in the back seat of a car. It's like . . . like he *forgot*. All she wanted him for was a model. What else? Because I'll tell you something about Taylor. He wasn't that good in bed. Not with women. He'd been at this too long. Some of his girlfriends used to complain. So what else could she want him for?'' Reno sat back and looked at Bryce as if he expected him to provide the answer.

''Tell me about his picture collection.''

''God, Taylor and his pictures.'' Reno threw back his head and laughed. ''Every time you turned around he was snapping some picture. Didn't care if you were bareassed or what. Didn't care if he even knew you. He just liked pictures. Even if he just met you, the first thing he asked for was a snapshot. I told him, 'Taylor, you should be a photographer, you'd make a fortune,' and he'd say, 'Yeah, you're right.' But he never did anything about it.''

''In those pictures, were there things that someone might find embarrassing? Might have made them want to get the pictures back or just make them disappear?''

Reno stared at him. ''I don't know. Some of them weren't, well, too *good*, if you know what I mean. But most of them were okay.''

''Do you know where the pictures are now?''

''Nope,'' the boy said, shaking his head. ''Keeping up with Taylor wasn't easy, you know? He's got stuff stashed all over this city. Wish I did know where it was. Had some nice pictures. I'd like to have some of them,'' he finished, looking absurdly young.

''He never showed you a picture of his friend?''

''Yeah,'' Reno said, scowling. ''Blond, skinny, pretty face. Had one in his wallet. Couple in some fancy frames. Just regular pictures.''

''When was the last time you saw him?''

''About three weeks before he went off the bridge. Met him at a bar and we went out and drank a six-pack on the beach—just the two of us. Sucker was just as cheerful as he could be. On top of the world, like a movie star. Had a brand new jacket I tried to talk him into giving me, but he wouldn't go for it. You know, there was this exhibit that opened at some fancy art place off Union Square—"

"I've seen it."

"Yeah, well, I don't know who painted it, but a lot of guys on the street thought that was really something. Big time, you know? One day guys were saying, we're gonna see Taylor up there on the silver screen. But . . . I wasn't so sure."

Bryce was more certain. Some of those street kids would glory in any kind of recognition. But what about a young man who wanted to play down that side of his life—who created a more sane, normal one using pictures of strangers? (Did he sit there and pretend they were his family? Make up more stories?) A man who liked the romance of movies—how would he feel about this glossless portrayal? A perishable quality, self-esteem, especially when it's new. But then he'd posed for them, hadn't he? Surely he *knew* what was coming. Or had he? Bryce felt his stomach knot, and his mouth suddenly tasted sour. He knew Reno's eyes were on him and wondered if the sickness he felt could be observed on his face. Bryce made a series of small, neat tears on the rim of his empty Styrofoam cup. Reno opened his mouth and drained his drink, which was now nothing but a brown stream of damp sugar.

"I got an old lady now. She's smart enough to have a regular job in a store, and sweet, you know? A little fat, but that's okay. Thinks she can get me a job in one of those movie houses downtown. We've been together three months now. That's a long time, y'know?" Reno said, as though refueling his optimism once more. "You got yourself an old lady, dude?"

Bryce wondered how Katharine would take being referred to as someone's old lady. He tried to imagine it. The raised eyebrows, the burst of laughter. He grinned.

"Yes," he said.

The kid nudged him with his elbow, a different touch from his last approach. Sexless, one man to another.

"Any kids?" Reno asked, as if it were an issue of genuine concern to him.

"No, not yet."

"But you're trying, eh? That's good. Kids are nice. I like kids. I was gonna have a kid once. The bitch went down and had him aborted. Can't blame her, I guess," he finished philosophically.

Bryce stared at his mutilated cup, then got up and threw it in a nearby garbage can. He put one foot on the bench and bent low. "Was there anyone who really disliked Taylor? Might have a grudge against him? Might have wanted to do him harm?"

"Sure. I mean, there were guys who didn't like him. There was some dude he smacked with a beer bottle once. Cracked his head open. Guy wasn't real happy," Reno catalogued cheerfully. "A few things like that. No big deal."

"Nobody out of the ordinary looking for him recently?"

"Only you." Reno chuckled. He tossed his cup in the direction of the trashcan, where it tipped the rim and drifted to the ground.

"And Taylor didn't leave anything for you? Sent you no messages?"

"No."

"Would you have any idea why there was nothing in his pockets—no wallet, nothing at all when he jumped?"

Reno shrugged. "Doesn't cost to jump, does it?"

"But you don't have any idea where his things might be? Did he often go out without anything, not even a penny?"

"It don't make sense, man. But I don't know the answers. He didn't leave no wallet with me. And the shades, man. He always had a pair in his pocket. But I don't know where they are or where his fucking collection is. I don't *know*," he repeated, and Bryce didn't know if he was lying or not. Life on the streets consisted of a series of lies. After a while they simply became habit. Reno knew something he wasn't saying, but what Bryce didn't know was whether that something was petty or important, left out by accident or design. "What's so important about that fucking collection, anyway?"

"Who else has been looking for it?"

The boy shrugged and got up off the bench. "Got to start heading back. Come on, old man. Tell you a story as good as Taylor could tell you."

They moved slowly out of the park, hands deep in their pockets. They walked like two scholars in deep discussion of some academic problem, scattering pigeons begging their last late afternoon meal, battling a sudden burst of cold wind.

"I was living with this Italian dude, off Steiner Street, you know. Sharing a place. I wasn't putting out," he evidently felt compelled to announce, "just kind of . . . we had an arrangement. Anyway, before I even know Taylor was dead, I meet this guy in a bar. Short, chubby little fart. He brought up Taylor's name real casual-like, said he knew him—I said I did, too, and he acted all happy, like it gave us something in common. Then he starts asking questions. Wanted to know where Taylor had been staying nowadays. I don't know, and that's what I tell him. He laughed and said something about being interested in seeing the collection. Probably some interesting stuff in it, you know? Yup, he said, be willing to *pay* to see that. And I tell you, old man, I been on the streets since I was twelve. This was no idle bullshit."

"But you had nothing to show?"

"Not a thing. Not one fucking thing. Believe me, I would have showed him if I had. I could've used the cash. But I didn't, and I told the guy that. So that morning I get home around three, maybe four, and hit the sack. Next day I'm out, come back to find this crazy Italian waiting up for me, and is he pissed. The place is a mess—totally wasted. Shit thrown all over the place. He blames me, we get in a fight, and pretty soon me and my suitcases are out the door. So I crash at my mom's. I'm good there for about two days. Well, you know what?"

"It happened there too?"

"You got it, old man. Then Angie tells me about Taylor. I get nervous, split town. Went to Santa Cruz for a couple weeks. Kept out of trouble. Angie says Taylor killed himself—which could be true. Moody, Taylor was. And getting old. When he was happy, he was the most beautiful person in the world, and when he wasn't, it was scary, you know? Anyway, who knew what the hell he'd been up to? Taylor'd talk to you about anything but the truth."

"Nobody's bothered you since?"

"Just you," Reno responded cheerily. No wonder Taylor kept up a friendship with Reno. Perhaps the boy's indefatigable good humor was Taylor's antidote for his own moodiness.

"Hey, old man, what's in those pictures, anyway?"

"I wish I knew," Bryce said.

Reno stole a sideways glance at him. "That stuff never *looked* like anything important."

"Looks can be deceiving," Bryce quoted for the second time in the last twenty-four hours, and felt depressingly redundant.

"But they aren't usually," Reno asserted.

Bryce looked at him sharply, and something in this expression made Reno take a step to one side, affording Bryce a clear view of the opposing street corner. He stopped.

"Who is that?"

"Who is who?" asked Reno, following Bryce's eyes to a young man, a milky-caramel color, an unspoiled beauty of high cheekbones and delicate nostrils, dressed in blue jeans and a leather jacket, lounging against a concrete wall. "Him? Jeez, old man, don't you know nothing? That's the Angel."

"Angel?"

"Yeah. That's what he's called. Real name's Gabriel. Like the angel, y'know?" Reno chuckled. "Kind of a *fallen* angel, eh? He's a regular around here. Like a lamp post."

"I've seen him before," said Bryce.

"Yeah, well, the Angel gets around."

"What's his reputation?"

''Not very friendly. Does his business and don't socialize. The Angel's the kind you go to if you want something kinkier than kinky. To tell you the truth, the guy gives me the creeps.''

Glancing across the street, Bryce thought, No, he doesn't look like a comfortable sort to have around. In an opera, Bryce would have cast him as an almost mystical figure. A Saint Germaine. He returned his attention to Reno.

''Did he know Taylor?''

Reno wrinkled his nose. ''They did some jobs together, but they weren't no bosom buddies.''

''Do you think Taylor would have introduced him to his friend?''

''Shit, no, man. Would you introduce him to your old lady? The guy's a spook—and I'm not talking about his color.''

''No one's talked about his likeness being in those paintings of Taylor?''

''People don't spend a lot of time talking about the Angel. They just let him be. Smartest thing to do.''

Bryce looked at Reno thoughtfully. ''Angie will have a present for you tonight,'' he said, and stuck out his hand. After a second's hesitation, Reno accepted it.

''Whatever you say. I'll be around, that's for sure.'' The boy turned away.

''Reno, how old was Taylor?''

Reno turned back, moving his fingers, calculating the figures with their help, somehow appearing older in the growing dark. ''Twenty.''

Bryce let him go. Reno grinned and waved and was soon lost as the first wave of PG&E employees poured out of their building.

Bryce glanced across the street. The corner was empty.

Chapter Eight

■

Before he went to his next appointment, Bryce made a detour to the gallery on Sutter Street, where he found himself studying the object of his afternoon's conversation. He moved from picture to picture, carefully examining each, down to the simple androgynous R. Gautier signed on the corner, aware of a growing sympathy for their subjects. But sympathy for the Devil or the betrayed? Looking at them made him aware of man's inhumanity to man, seemed to transfer their feelings of isolation laced with the kind of self-disgust that often follows sex indulged in without the condiment of respect, much less love. When it is reduced to an act of hedonism, packaged like a hamburger from McDonald's.

In her paintings the clients were hazy, as if blurred by how speedily they were replaced. The face of the male prostitute, however, had been made distinct by the disturbing, ultimately lonely emotions depicted on his perfect features. In some, the tangle of beauty and ugliness, hope and hopeless, became grotesque. Bryce was particularly struck by a painting in which Taylor seemed to have caught himself by surprise in a mirror, as if he found the sight of himself shocking and wanted to look away, but couldn't.

There was something in the perspective of these paintings that intrigued him. Gautier had mentioned Kirchner on their first meeting. But no Kirchner streetwalker ever had the individuality of Roxanne's. Kirchner might have presented his with a certain familiarity, the understanding perhaps of one social outcast to another, but not with Roxanne's clarity of emotion. Her representation seemed to be that of the prostitutes themselves. Her paintings reflected the frank kind of physical observation he had observed in Reno, but also reflected how the imagination, the heart, warred with the ultimate pragmatism of selling yourself.

Bryce moved on to the next canvas. But now it was not Taylor's face that drew him, but the face worked dimly into the shadows. The Angel's face was a sad but sinister presence. What had he to do with this? And how had Roxanne discovered him? Not in the hall of any Academy of Art, certainly.

Suddenly something that should have been obvious to him sooner struck him with overwhelming impact. He walked the exhibition over quickly and discovered he was correct. The exhibit, called *On Polk*, was divided into three sections. The first, "Day Scenes," was self-explanatory. The second, "Transitions," followed the street's changes from day to night, the migration of daytime inhabitants and the takeover of night ones. The third was called "Views from a Window." While Taylor appeared in all three sections, he was spotlighted in the third. But Bryce saw not Taylor, but Paul Gautier sitting across from him talking earnestly, as he had that first afternoon.

. . . her subjects are now prostitutes—male prostitutes . . . and murder . . .

Portrayed here, Bryce saw prostitution, theft, brutality, coquetry, a broad sampling of human vices and emotions.

But not murder.

* * *

The burst of energy and resolution that sent Bryce out the gallery door left him empty and discouraged on the other side. He wandered a few paces down the street before he stopped to stare into a shop window.

He'd been approached by a suspicious husband who suspected his wife, but of what, he didn't know. He had a confession but no crime. Someone was ransacking apartments for an apparently harmless collection of photographs. To top it all, his dinner date for the evening was, in his own mind, becoming a monster whose proportions could only be equaled by Medusa. Oh lovely, lovely. Shall we be known by our companions? If so, that left him in an ambiguous position.

Someone bumped him and mumbled an apology before continuing down the street. It was getting dark, a condition in keeping with Bryce's mood. He walked on behind a woman holding the hand of a small child whose other hand clutched the string of a balloon printed with the logo of The Christmas Store. It bobbed up and down in front of Bryce like a guiding star.

Laura Parnismus, whose beautiful face was attached to an overly well-rounded body, appraised Kevin Bryce in her usual glowing fashion.

"Kevin, darling, you look wonderful," she said as, to his surprise, she stood to embrace him and kiss his cheek, enveloping him in the sweet scent of Oscar de la Renta. Then she stood back and took another look. "Katharine must be buying your clothes," she announced before sliding back in the booth, settling in the center, to preside in the manner of a queen over her subjects.

"You get an A in deduction," he said.

"It's the collars," Laura explained. "It's always the collars that give a person away. Yours are positively avant-garde compared to what you were wearing before."

"Shopping for clothes bores me," he confessed, slipping in to his place to her left.

"Well, you needn't worry," she assured him. Although until that moment it had never occurred to him to give it any thought at all. It had been at his instigation that Katharine had begun choosing his clothes. "You're in very good hands. I hope you plan on staying in them."

"Which is supposed to mean what?" Dear Laura, he thought, don't spoil your image of gossipy free spirit and suddenly become meddlesome.

"It means exactly what it says. Oh lovely, here comes the champagne. I ordered champagne," she explained. "I love champagne. And oysters. I ordered them both. That's what you get for being late."

"This is punishment?"

"It will be to your pocketbook," she told him smugly. The remark was punctuated with the pop of the champagne cork. Bryce wondered how some women could be such complete pains in the ass and still remain likable.

Laura tipped her glass against his. "To the exchange of information."

"Exchange?"

She looked at him, then put down her glass. "Oh, Kevin, *don't* tell me you're going to be stingy."

He sipped his drink, taking the time to reflect that Laura did have expensive taste and to observe out of the corner of his eye that a fat nymph on the mural behind their booth seemed to regard them with interest.

"Did you talk to Roxanne? Is that what made you think I'd call? Then I have to assume she was asking about me?"

"Yes, yes, and yes again," she answered. "She came in this morning and was looking through some back issues of the paper—"

"For what, specifically? Do you know?"

"Yes, as a matter of fact, I do," she said triumphantly. "Found out from the librarian. Roxanne was checking up on the Lake Tahoe art robberies. And then," she continued sweetly, tapping her glass, "she just happens by my office. Those articles don't say much, but they did mention my husband and me. She oh-so-discreetly mentioned who her dinner guest was the night before, and we're off to a flying start. She, trying to pry out of me all your nasty secrets, and me, flustered because I had none to tell—or none that I *could* tell. I had to be somewhat discreet. After all, you're practically family. I considered making some up, but nothing, unfortunately, seemed as interesting as the truth. Of course, it was only ten in the morning, and I'm never very creative until after noon. It's my biorhythms. Oh, lovely, here are the oysters!" She placed both hands flat on the table and peered down at the plate. Then she awarded the waiter—a small, stooped man—her most beautiful smile. He left pleased, but flustered. "Silly old boy," she remarked. "You do like oysters, yes?"

Bryce nodded laconically. "I've gotten over the fact they look like sludge in a shell."

"You have an almost obscene way of dampening a person's spirits," she remarked, then cheerfully speared an oyster with a fork, and after dotting it with horse radish, and cocktail sauce, swallowed it whole.

"You have to admit they are an acquired taste."

"I suppose. Rather like caviar. Or men. They have the same things in common. You know there's something fishy about them, but after a while you don't care."

Brycc groaned.

"Now," she said, primly spotting the corners of her mouth with her napkin, "I suppose I'm to tell you all of Roxanne's nasty secrets."

"I'll take a little of her background first, if you have it," he suggested, taking an oyster, shell and all.

"Father was a doctor in one of those grim Los Angeles suburbs. Mother died when she was a teenager. I've heard rumors it was in Napa State, but since those rumors came from her in-laws . . ." With magnificent eloquence, Laura shrugged her large shoulders. "No brothers, no sisters. Went to several art schools, and somewhere in between, went to the Academy of Art here, where at some social function or other she met Paul Gautier." Laura frowned, selecting another oyster.

"It was Katharine who introduced them; I was there. Paul, I thought, was getting rather attached to Katharine—I think that might be why she introduced Roxanne to him, as a diversion. Katharine met his family once and, believe me, was not interested in becoming a member of it. Anyway, Paul and Roxanne were married six months later."

"Happily?" Bryce asked.

"Apparently."

"You sound as if you harbor some doubt, Laura."

"I always harbor doubt about marital bliss. Even my own," she confessed. "And I believe I *am* happily married." Laura fueled herself with more champagne before she continued. "Paul, I remember, was quite smitten with her when they met. He can be a very forceful person when he's convinced about something."

"And he was convinced he should marry Roxanne and live happily ever after?"

"A bizarre way to put it, but probably correct. I think he viewed Roxanne as something exotic. Anyway, her feelings seemed to me a little more difficult to determine. Outwardly she is always affectionate. But then again..."

"But then again, what?"

Laura speared another oyster, a particularly fat one, and halfway through its trip to her mouth, changed her mind. She balanced her fork carefully on her bread and butter plate.

"Roxanne always knows the right thing to do, but sometimes one wonders how *sincere* it all is. She has a dry sense of humor that's amusing, but I get the feeling it may be a little more mean-spirited than anyone realizes. At times her observations are a little too pointed and altogether too accurate. But she does have the ability to zero in on what is going to entertain a person, and she uses it."

Bryce's expression became so serious that he gave the impression of being angry. Laura looked at him curiously, reflecting that Kevin Bryce was a peculiar sort himself. She had to take her hat off to Katharine. He was more than she would like to have to cope with every day. Although he might be fun to fool around with. For a weekend or so.

"Any more judicious conclusions?" Bryce asked, startling Laura, who thought he had been reading her mind.

"Yes," she said, composing herself. "She's too thin. Is it Bernard Shaw who has the line about lean and hungry men—they think too much and are too ambitious?—I think that's the gist of it. Or was it Socrates?"

"Shakespeare. It's from *Julius Caesar*."

"How well-informed you are," she said. "Anyway, that is what she always makes me think of. As far as her reputation goes, it's almost unblemished. At least, I think it is."

"What do you mean by 'almost' unblemished?" He sat back and regarded her seriously.

Laura, to her own surprise, found herself fidgeting. This must be how he interrogated his suspects, she thought. Thank God, I'm not guilty of anything. Or not of much.

"Well, this last show of hers—you've seen it, I assume?—it's causing a lot of talk. It *is* a little bizarre. And, I mean, it's so . . ." Words, in a rare instance, failed her. ". . . I mean, you could hardly fail to get the point. A lot of people are asking a lot of silly questions about how and why. And Paul's family! You have to understand what you're dealing with here. Paul comes from a very well-respected family—a family with very conventional attitudes on life. Believe me, none of those kids were ever handed anything—they had to work for it. His family was astonished when Paul married Roxanne. They expect him to go for meat and potatoes, and instead he makes a meal out of a Bloody Mary. Paul is a good and dutiful son, but he has a mind of his own."

"And his wife gets the blame whenever he strays a little off course?"

"What else? Although I doubt if Roxanne would dream of influencing him. She doesn't have that much interest in anything besides her work. But you have to give his family credit," she continued ironically. "They were willing to get used to the idea, if she painted nice little still lifes or landscapes, or potted flowers. Something that would conform to their idea of what should be hung in the living room. Her mother-in-law has always encouraged her to do family portraits—although God only knows what family portraits by Roxanne might turn into."

Laura was relieved to see Kevin break into a grin. "And how did Roxanne react to this?"

"Very politely. But I was always under the impression she went into a quiet room afterward and smashed things."

"There has never been any more specific gossip?"

"No. Although there are some people who sniped that she spent more time with one of her young models than was healthy. But I think that was just talk. After all, Paul spent time with him too. His brother Rob told me he used to take the boy sailing with them. And, believe me, knowing Paul, I don't think he would back her up like that if he didn't think everything was open and aboveboard. Paul isn't that tolerant."

Bryce drank his champagne and mulled over the presentation Gautier had given him. It seemed Gautier had made a lot of tactful omissions.

"So there's my word of warning," Laura said, as if, like Pontius Pilate, she was washing her hands of the whole affair.

"You think I'm in need of one?" he asked.

Laura found the sudden amusement in his eyes disconcerting. "Hard telling," she answered truthfully. "What *are* you in town for, may I ask?"

"Petter thought he had a buyer for my Tahoe property."

"What do you mean 'thought'? Petter is usually very sure about these sorts of things."

"It's the seller he's having problems with," Bryce said, reverting to the dignity of the third person. "He's not sure he wants to sell. Especially when the choice of buyers include a possible drug dealer and an old despot."

"Goodness. It's just a piece of property. Does it really matter?"

Bryce shrugged. "It was special in its time," he said thoughtfully. "It's like—well, like an old mistress. Just because you no longer want her," he ventured almost innocently, "doesn't mean you're willing to sell her off to a pimp."

Laura gaped. "Well," she said a little breathlessly, "I'll have to tell Katharine. I'm sure she'll find that comforting."

Bryce whimsically regarded the way her fork was poised in a delicate arch in midair.

"Do you think so?" he asked. *Would you think so if you knew that Katharine has never once—never* once*—said 'I love you'?* "She's much more likely to get rid of me than I am of her."

This statement caused Laura to put down her fork. She nearly dropped it. "What's this? Self-*doubt*?"

"We all have occasional bouts of it," he remarked.

He did not feel disposed to explain it was not so much a matter of self-doubt as an inclination to take one's own temperature. To keep in perspective any delusions of grandeur, always to guard against the possibility of unexpected pain.

Laura took great large gulps of champagne before she pointed her fork at him.

"Maybe that's what makes you seem more human than Roxanne. That touch of doubt and uncertainty. She doesn't seem to have it."

Listening to her Bryce had the impression Laura was drawing comparisons between himself and Roxanne. And why not? Hadn't Laura observed him during the Tahoe investigation? In the police role not allowing himself to feel too much, and not allowing what little he did feel to get in the way of what had to be done.

Even now, he was peering over Roxanne's shoulder into her life in much the same way Roxanne had done to Taylor.

"Petter is having dinner with Ed and me this evening. Would you like to join us?"

In the second before he answered, it occurred to him that with all her talking, Roxanne evidently hadn't said a word to Laura about dinner that night. That was interesting. Neither had he. He decided to keep it that way.

"No, thank you very much, but I have plans."

Laura opened her mouth and then closed it without asking the question Bryce wouldn't have answered anyway.

"Well, since I've been providing all the salient information and you've been offering essentially very little—"

"Except for the champagne and oysters," he noted dryly.

"Yes, but you've been stingy with information. So—will you do me a favor and take James's Christmas presents from us back to Ireland with you? If I mail them, they might not get there in time."

James Parnismus, Laura's brother-in-law and Bryce's literary partner, was shuffling between Bryce's home in Ireland and a girlfriend in London in whom he had dubious interest. James's thoughts and emotions were often dubious, well-camouflaged by his comedian's touch, by his cheerfulness and good humor—like Reno, if one cared to make an outlandish comparison, Bryce thought. And maybe, in an even more outlandish and limited comparison, Bryce played a Taylor to James's Reno. Bryce had no doubt Taylor had used Reno shamelessly, as perhaps he had also done to James. Together they had produced five controversial novels and had another in the works. But at Kevin's insistence, only James's name appeared on the finished product, so it was James who was subjected to both public praise and outrage, who had to appear intelligent in interviews, who found notes from admiring fans or outraged detractors under his windshield wipers, who had his privacy pried apart and was forced to be gracious to strangers. While Bryce was able to preserve his solitude, take pleasure in his work and his profits, in relative peace. To be fair, although he sometimes resented it, James basically enjoyed the hullabaloo and was naturally gracious, a movie's conception of a best-selling author, good looks and all. Still, if James hadn't enjoyed it, Bryce wondered, would it have made any difference?

"Yes, of course. Just drop them by my hotel whenever you like."

"Good. I will, as soon as I buy them." Her eyes scanned the room. "Where is that waiter? No sense of timing. Typically male," she said. It was characteristic of Laura to reduce the world's problems to the differences between men and women.

"Don't tell me you want more champagne."

"No, the phone book. I'm supposed to meet Ed and Petter at some restaurant, but I can't remember which one. It started with a D though, I do remember that."

Bryce got the waiter's attention and Laura was supplied with the phone book. At she studied its pages, the conversation took a slightly different turn.

"One thing about Roxanne, you have to give her credit," Laura said offhandedly. "For a straight woman to attempt a commentary on the gay world takes a lot of—something, I'm not sure what."

"You really think those paintings are a commentary on gay lifestyles?"

"You don't?"

"No," he said, thoughtfully touching the rim of his glass with his thumb. "I think they're commenting on a more basic issue."

"And what issue is that?"

"Hocking your ass."

Laura looked up from her book, licking her thumb, and though her face did not reveal it, she marveled at the capability he had for turning the harshest analysis into perfectly acceptable, even gentle, conversation.

"If she is addressing the issue of prostitution itself, then why present it this way? It seems an unusual position from which to view it. Especially for a woman who has no homosexual leanings. Or no public ones, anyway,'' she amended, lest she be found ignorant of some private peccadillo.

"Maybe,'' Bryce said slowly, "because that was what was making itself available.'' He paused. "It might have been the most discreet way to approach the issue.''

"I must say you have peculiar ideas of discretion. Considering the effect of the exhibit, would you care to revise that?''

"No,'' he said, giving the softness of his delivery a decisive edge. "Some eruptions are easier to handle than others.''

"She hasn't seemed to have any problems handling this one,'' Laura admitted, her finger suddenly halting its long progress down the page. "There's the place!''

Bryce paid the bill and he and Laura left the restaurant. Outside, they stopped for a minute, making a small, still oasis among the throngs of Christmas shoppers, listening to the echo of the carolers singing "God Rest Ye Merry Gentlemen'' on the bottom floor of the Galleria. Before they parted, Laura repeated a question she had already posed in various forms.

"I still don't understand. If you're right and she was going to pick prostitution as a theme—why use men?'' She turned her beautiful puzzled face to Kevin, demanding an answer.

He smiled, but his answer was almost brusque.

"Why not? Misery doesn't have a gender.''

Chapter Nine

■

February 17—

I had never met anyone like Paul before. He was level-headed and kind, the first man I'd ever met who really listened. Within a week we were seeing each other every day. When he told me he'd fallen in love with me on first sight, I laughed, sure it was a romantic exaggeration. He was easy to talk to, although sometimes he would dig deeper than I wanted him to go—and was difficult to discourage. But he had an unwavering faith in my artistic ability, was adamant that I continue in art. He was the best friend I'd ever had.

Five months later he asked me to marry him. When I said no, he said he didn't want to see me anymore.

I hadn't realized how much I'd come to depend on his company. But I wasn't "in love," felt no passion. I called him on the phone, told him I'd move in with him. But he said no, he wanted commitment.

I hung up, got into bed, and pulled the covers over my head.

I have always shied away from promises. They seem inherently untrustworthy. This was the first time I'd ever encountered a demand from someone I couldn't abandon. Loneliness had always been second nature to me, but suddenly there was an urgent sense of loss. What was worse—I couldn't seem to work.

I took a bottle of Wild Turkey to Katharine's, drinking over half of it while she sipped some from a shot glass. I never told Katharine what was on my mind. Out of perversity, I imitated Katharine's own lack of explanation. But I'm sure I gave her many looks of keen accusation before I passed out on her worktable.

Paul and I were married a month later.

At first we didn't have much money, he was just starting in business, and made sacrifices for my work that I knew I would never make for his. I felt—still feel—that his goodness subtly demanded the same from me. And got it—on the surface. On the inside it produced something I hadn't felt in years.

I'd go to bed with him, tell him I loved him. I'd lie beside him afterward, knowing that compared to the kind of response he expected of me, I was a liar. I'd fall asleep to the chant liar, liar, liar . . .

Paul began to make a lot of money, and I devoted myself entirely to painting. Though I did sell a few, it was due to Paul's earnings that we began to change our lifestyle. We bought an apartment that had a room perfect for a studio for me.

But I was restless. Bored? Not in my studio. Never in my studio. My work was well-received, selling more all the time. I had become used to the best materials, and, most of all, the time and privacy I required. How could I possibly give that up?

*One night when Paul and I had finished making love, he put his hand on the left side of my chest. Never, in all my life, had I felt more angry. No, more than just angry—*violated. *This was no tender lover's gesture. He was checking on me, trying to determine if our activity had made any difference. My heartbeat* *was normal, rhythmic, quiet. I had read a book once where, in bed with his wife, a man brought his hand around and with the flat of his palm broke her nose as she lay beside him. One single, timely gesture. I wished I could do that to Paul. Instead, I gently took his hand and kissed it, curled in the crook of his arm and feigned sleep.*

In time Roxanne would, once again, take a class at the Academy of Art, make use of the models provided. So many of her social contacts had become business—gallery business, Paul's friends and family, that it was nice to go back, to listen to the enthusiasm of young artists. That was where she would first see Taylor; he was the model. She didn't like the look of him; his kind of classical perfection bored her. But she stayed the entire session, afterward going to a café with someone from class, Alicia. She was a short woman, with sultry Latin looks and, Roxanne suspected, somewhat unhealthy taste in entertainment. They ordered wine and chatted about nothing of any importance, until Roxanne saw Alicia's face change, taking on the sort of smoldering look she associated with badly performed productions of *Carmen*. Roxanne followed her gaze, saw Taylor coming through the door, and was amused to see that Taylor evidently missed the point. His eyes went over Alicia without any sign of recognition, then he sat with a man and woman with whom he seemed well-acquainted. Roxanne was to learn later he seemed well-acquainted with nearly everyone.

Alicia smirked. "Guess he doesn't give it away," she said.

"Why? Does he usually charge?" Roxanne asked dryly.

"As a matter of fact, he does," she said, and without prompting, launched into an amazingly detailed account of his reputation. Roxanne wasn't much impressed by his history, but she listened carefully, noting Alicia's excited face, wondering how much time she'd spent studying this young man in pursuit of vicarious thrills.

* * *

There was a bookstore adjacent to the café, up a small flight of stairs. Finishing her drink, Roxanne went there for a book Paul had ordered for his nephew's birthday, a special edition of Tolkien's *The Hobbit*. She came down the stairs just as Taylor was coming up, watching his feet on the steps, his forehead wrinkled. Something earnest and cautious about this posture reminded her of one of Paul's young nephews learning to take the stairs; tentative, because his mother has admonished him to be careful; struggling to gain confidence. Taylor looked up suddenly and, again, like one of Paul's nephews, he smiled. And she thought: He at least has that going for him.

A few weeks later Paul and Roxanne were on the family boat at the St. Francis Yacht Harbor. It was a rainy Saturday noon, and they had been there since early Friday morning preparing the boat for an outing the next day, which was supposed to be sunny. Roxanne's job that day was to entertain Paul while he did his various projects, to hand him a tool when he asked, occasionally to hold a tape measure. The next day was to be spent with her in-laws. Given other considerations, she figured it would be Tuesday before she would get back to her paints. She tried to read, but could feel herself growing restless and irritable. Paul was on the floor, flat on his back, fiddling with the heater. She looked out the porthole at the other boats bobbing up and down, and wondered how anyone could find this a pleasurable hobby. Not that she had anything against the great outdoors, she reasoned. On the contrary, she loved nature—until it started crawling up her pant leg, swimming down the front of her bathing suit, or rocking her into nausea.

Paul was laughing.

"What's so funny?" she asked.

When he regained control of himself, he said: "Are you

thinking of the fun you'll have listening to Mother tell you how wonderful I am?''

''Sometimes I wish I had a mother so I could lock you up with her in a padded cell,'' she replied, and he started laughing again. ''Sometimes I wish you would say 'fuck' in front of yours just so I could see her face.''

Paul remained cheerful. ''I don't say that when I'm alone—why should I say it for Mom's benefit?''

And what she found so discouraging was that she knew he was telling the truth.

''Listen,'' he said, and Roxanne could see he was weighing things carefully, trying to be fair. ''Why don't you get out for a while? Go shopping or to the movies, take a walk.''

''You don't mind?'' she asked, knowing he did.

''I'll live,'' he said. ''Besides, you've been a good girl for a day and a half. I'm too practical to push my luck.'' He paused. ''I'm not asking much, Rox. Just one day.''

''No,'' she said quickly.

''And you enjoy Rob.''

It was true. She did enjoy Rob, though the rest of them bored her.

''I should be done around five. I'll tell you what—we can walk to Mulhern's and I'll buy you dinner. If I feed you enough hot toddies, do you think you can survive tomorrow?''

''Given enough hot toddies, I can survive anything,'' she said, mocking a brave face.

She walked to Chestnut Street. Thunder clapped overhead, there was the urgent scream of a siren, a dog howled. The sweet, yeasty smell of fresh doughnuts tempted her from an old storefront; displays of shoes, clothes, and books graced other windows. People rushed from the buildings to their cars, heads protected with newspapers, hats, umbrellas. Her shoes felt damp and heavy, and as she passed a theater, she could smell popcorn, the aroma so alluring that she ducked under the overhang. The movie started in ten minutes. She purchased a ticket, some hot chocolate, and a huge tub of popcorn.

She took the second seat from the aisle, leaving her wet slicker on the first. Taking off her shoes, she hung her feet over a heater vent to dry, then warmed her hands around the cup of chocolate. When they were sufficiently thawed, she exchanged the cup for the popcorn and began to eat, one kernel at a time.

The movie was a revival of Lina Wertmuller's *Seven Beauties*. It was just starting when someone slipped into the theatre and, selecting the closest aisle seat, sat heavily on Roxanne's wet slicker.

"*Shit!*"

Roxanne, suppressing a giggle, tried to compose her face into something apologetic. She moved quickly to set the popcorn on the floor and grab for the slicker, but in her hurry she hit her elbow against the side of the seat, spilling half the tub onto the man's lap. Surprised, his foot kicked out, knocking over the chocolate, sending a hot splash over Roxanne's feet. She countered his profanity with one of her own, pulled her slicker out from under him, and for the first time looked at the man's face, halfway prepared for a fight. Roxanne and Taylor stared at one another. He seemed surprised and—what? A little suspicious? No, calculating, as if he were assessing the situation, deciding how best to react; with a jolt, he reminded Roxanne of herself. He looked at his lap, took some popcorn between his fingers and popped it into his mouth.

"It's nice of you to share, but I prefer it out of the tub," he said, swallowing.

She held up her empty chocolate cup for him to see.

"Get me a replacement and you can have your preference," she told him, and they both laughed. A woman in front turned to hush them. Taylor grinned, and after a pause, the woman settled back in her seat without further comment.

Taylor winked at Roxanne before he got up and went to the snack bar.

He had dinner with Paul and Roxanne that night, telling endless stories about people at the academy and encounters with people on the street that might have hinted at his other life if they hadn't been told with such humor, been so obviously exaggerated. Under less civilized circumstances Paul might have wondered about a young man who spent so much time walking the streets, in such diversified company. For Roxanne it was a relief to be entertained instead of being the one doing the entertaining. But she assumed it wouldn't happen again—the movie, the dinner, a friendly nod in class from then on . . . If there hadn't been a small incident—something that could have easily been ignored.

The three of them were standing under the canvas awning of the restaurant, saying good-bye. A taxi pulled up, and from out of it came a man, well-dressed and conspicuously gay, flaunting it as if it were a medal of honor rather than a mere sexual preference. Taylor retreated a step, but there was no place to hide. The two knew each other, of course. The look the man gave Taylor was knowledgeable, even inviting. In another moment he would approach. Roxanne saw something pass over Taylor's face, brief, as quick as a cloud can blot the sun's light. She saw self-hatred.

She took a step, placing herself between the two men, and linked her arm through Taylor's. She started telling a joke, a terrible joke, and got it all mixed up so she could appeal to Paul for help, all the while guiding Taylor down the street—herself on one side, Paul on the other—away from the man, who eventually disappeared into the restaurant. Two blocks from the harbor Paul and Taylor started talking about boats. Paul and Roxanne exchanged a look, and Paul invited Taylor to join them on the next day's outing.

* * *

Later, entangled with Paul on a bunk that went up and down with every wave and flutter of the water beneath them, Roxanne tried to sleep despite her queasy stomach. She held Paul as if he were her life preserver.

"Rox," he said. "I thought you said Taylor was a model for the Academy of Art."

"He is."

"But that's not his only occupation."

"No," she said. "But I could hardly introduce him at dinner as a part-time model and full-time . . . well, it wouldn't seem polite, would it?" she pointed out; quite reasonably, in her opinion.

"I should have known." He sighed.

Poor Paul. He'd had to stretch himself a lot in the past few years, develop a broadmindedness Roxanne was sure he'd never considered. He amazed her. It wasn't really in his nature to invite handsome young call boys to dinner with his wife. It would never have occurred to him on his own. She was sure somewhere deep inside, he disapproved of himself.

"There isn't anything else I should know, is there? He doesn't axe-murder babies and leave them to rot in the forest by the Palace of the Legion of Honor, does he?"

"Sarcasm doesn't become you," she told him, and moved her head to rest on his stomach. She kissed his belly because she liked the texture of his hair against his skin. Also it curled her into a tighter ball, which she hoped would relieve some of her nausea.

"We have a transvestite housemaid and now Taylor to lunch with Mother—you make my life so interesting, Rox," he said, with more irony than sarcasm. It was that irony that Roxanne adored. Without it he would have been so tiresome she would have left him a long time ago. "You got a very bizarre sense of humor, Rox. You're enjoying the idea of my mother and him together, aren't you?"

She really hadn't thought of it before, but since he mentioned it—"Yes, I suppose I am."

And she did. It was definitely one of the more entertaining sessions she'd ever had with her in-laws. Just the idea of his family rubbing elbows with Taylor was enough to keep her the life of the party. Her father-in-law was convinced she was drunk, though she could see he was enjoying himself. Her mother-in-law looked at her with wide eyes, magnified further by thick spectacles. Paul's nieces and nephews were too young to think—at an age where they wet their pants and made noises only their mothers could interpret. But Paul's brothers and sisters naturally assumed she would, one day soon, be certifiable. Except for Rob. Roxanne did not think it was Rob's great regard for her, as much as his general disregard for the rest of the family. Rob was soft and jolly, lovable and slightly malicious, driving his mother crazy by telling her he was a confirmed bachelor, that she'd get no grandbabies out of him, as Roxanne watched him cheat at Monopoly. Distracted, neither his mother nor anyone else noticed.

Looking back on it, Roxanne thought Taylor must have assumed they were all one big happy family, a Christmas-card image. He had brought a camera, and took pictures. He appeared wholesome and healthy. Maybe he imagined himself as part of a scene from an old movie, one that celebrated the family. Roxanne's in-laws thought him charming; especially Rob, who had a real appreciation for beautiful things. Taylor looked at Paul with something akin to awe and was nice to Paul's mother, once playfully pinching her cheek, which made her chuckle and blush.

By the end of the day he was calling her Mom.

After class Roxanne and Taylor would go to a café for a drink (Alicia soon stopped speaking to her). Sometimes they'd go to a movie together, usually something Paul wasn't interested in seeing. And perhaps it was here that they established a precedent for their relationship that was a peculiar part of the attraction for Taylor. The odd draw was money. He never got any.

Oh, he tried to con her once. But you can't con a con. Roxanne was too good a manipulator not to recognize the technique—the plausible but somehow feeble excuse, the wishful sigh, the appealing look, the beginning of a pattern.

She recognized it one night when Paul had a business meeting and she and Taylor went to a movie and a late supper; then came time to figure the bill.

"Listen," he said, frowning as if he were dealing with an important problem. "This is always such a pain. Why don't we work it out some other way? I'll splurge one time and you splurge the next." He took out his wallet and checked his cash. Then he checked the bill. He checked his cash again. He gazed at Roxanne with guileless appeal. Roxanne found that his looks were growing on her. Now they were no longer an example of vacuous beauty, but a remarkable surface that reflected whatever he saw. Innocence, however improbable, was an appearance he could conjure at will. His sweetness was so genuine she had to suppose he believed all his own lies. But charming as it was, she never mistook any of it for sincerity. And she genuinely admired its entertainment value.

"Do you suppose . . ." he began, and she laughed. Roxanne reached across the table, tousling his hair even though she thought it might irritate him; his hair was always perfect.

"No," she told him cheerfully. "Absolutely not."

He never brought up the subject again.

What did they have to converse about? Everyday things. Movies. The unusual people that litter the streets of San Francisco. The art class—though eventually Roxanne stopped going. The pleasure Taylor took in his hours there was obvious. He enjoyed being the center of attention and, Roxanne was sure, preferred the idea of viewing himself through the eyes of others. She never saw him deliberately look in a mirror, and if by accident he caught sight of his reflection in a windowpane, he would quickly look away.

He was a young man for whom movies had played the role of father and mother. Roxanne was sure his social graces had been learned from the movies—that he had any, she learned later, was one of the things that separated him, put him a cut above a lot of the other boys on the street. He possessed a repertoire of personalities that changed every day and expanded with every movie he saw. Roxanne never knew if she would be greeted by Brando or Bogart or Depardieu, and liked to spend time with him because he was so interesting to watch. He aroused her curiosity. Was there anything real about him? If you pinched him, would he hurt? Or was he just a surface that reflected pain or anger or joy? When she touched Paul, her hand hit something solid—if she touched Taylor, would her hand slip right through?

When she was out alone, she took to driving down Polk, sometimes to a bookstore specializing in used books, pretending to look for a specific volume just so she could observe the customers. Later she went so she could watch the aging proprietor carry on lovingly with a thin calico cat, discussing her habits with his varied clientele.

"Camille, my lovely, do come in, *do,*" he'd plead with her as she threatened to wander out onto the sidewalk. He'd shoot water from a small bottle on his desk and she would scurry back. "To train her to stay *inside,*" he'd explain to an inquiring customer. "She doesn't like the water, do you, lovey?"

Roxanne would listen to him prattle in his happy fashion, would engage him directly in conversation to study the full view of his bagging eyes with their sandy lashes, the lines camouflaged by the cut of his fine, graying blond hair, his carefully trimmed moustache, the pale mole under the corner of his left eye, the unexpected wrinkles there which could not be described as laugh lines.

Was this an example of Taylor's clientele? And the boys on the street—were they his associates? She watched them carefully and saw hardness in their faces. Immaturity. Fear. Sometimes the normal naughtiness of any teenage boy taken several stages too far. Sometimes a face would exhibit the conceit of the criminal—the code of the street; every man for himself. These were Taylor's roots. What roles did he imitate here?

It was something to wonder at.

CHAPTER TEN

■

The St. Francis Yacht Harbor consists of an ineffectual breakwater sheltering rows of boat docks and a long green. There are two sections of harbor, one at each end of the green, and the boats' masts rose out of the darkness like a forest of leafless birch trees. Illuminated by a few weak security lights, the damp air glistened around them like snow. The boats, creaking and moaning, rode each small wave to its crest and slipped easily into their valleys. Here and there a small decorated tree was visible, set in a window in a foil-covered coffee can; or a wreath of pine branches and red ribbon had been hung off a convenient post by a festive sailor.

It was to the far end of the harbor, the old section closest to the bridge, that the dark-clothed figure walked noiselessly in rubber-soled shoes. Whether the figure came from the row of distinguished homes across the street or had sprung miraculously from the trees surrounding the Palace of Fine Arts—a romantic piece of architecture—was impossible to determine. At one of the dock gates it produced a key and entered, shutting the gate firmly behind.

It walked with the delicate determination of the runner, poised on the ball of the foot rather than the heel, bent forward slightly, arms held close to the waist. And like a determined runner, it made its way through the network of docks to a berth tucked between those of two massive cruisers, where it leapt deftly upon a large motor sailer, a dark shadow passing quickly across the white deck. Then a light went on briefly and was extinguished. And the vessel, wobbly and unstable on its liquid base, shifted violently from side to side.

Katharine, Bryce decided, was right. Roxanne was anorexic. The long-sleeved, high-necked dress of the night before had hidden much. But tonight, in the warmth of the restaurant, she had removed her coat and eventually also a light jacket. Underneath, matching the jacket, she was wearing a black shift, short-sleeved and V-necked, saved from shapelessness by some secret artistry of the designer. Elegant prison garb, Bryce privately dubbed it. Her arms sprouted out of the sleeves like delicate twigs, and the V neck revealed no cleavage, only a lightly outlined series of bones. Bryce imagined that lying naked with her, you could take the time and count every one of her ribs. So fragile seemed her physical structure, he felt that if he scooped her up into his arms she might crumble as easily as a sand castle. Only the face, despite its elegant bones, and the hands—those large, discolored paws—betrayed her strength.

They sat at a corner table in a dark and rustic restaurant. It was dark because people liked it that way, rustic not out of any decorator's vision but because it was genuinely old. It was a small place with no more than a dozen tables, each covered with bright blue tablecloths with white dusters peeking underneath as coyly as a woman's slip. The place was set on the piers in an as yet unfashionable but soon-to-be refurbished district. Outside the windows large tugs were docked, rocking gently to the tide. The food was fish, and good; the wine, respectable; the atmosphere clandestine without being sleazy.

During dinner Bryce was aware of her cautious and subtle probing—like the intricate balancing of weights or measures. He admired her oblique way of questioning him; so it was not for lack of patience, but his gut conviction, that to keep her a little off guard would be effective in drawing her respect.

"Did you find Laura informative this morning?" he asked bluntly.

Roxanne dabbed the corners of her mouth with her napkin and looked sorrowful. "Alas, no. I was the victim of misinformation."

He looked at her with a hint of both amusement and suspicion. "Oh? How so?"

She put her napkin back across her lap neatly. "Laura told me you were like a woman. That you worked by intuition. Now I find that's not entirely true. You also use a network."

"Every investigative endeavor has to have some kind of network. Ask any suburban housewife, and she'll be able to tell you all about the relay of information. And I'm sorry if I've disappointed you."

"Oh, I'm not disappointed. Do you know a lot about suburban housewives?"

"Perhaps suburban housewife was a poor illustration. Maybe a better one would be the street people. They also enjoy their share of gossip and conjecture."

"Do they, now? I can't say I find that surprising." Roxanne began playing with the food on her plate, particularly the vegetables, arranging them according to color.

"No," he said kindly, "I didn't suppose you would."

She looked up at him quickly.

"You do an excellent job of showing the viewpoint of the street."

"And I suppose you want to know how I know," she replied, keeping her derision in check.

Bryce shook his head slowly, settling back to allow the waiter to clear his plate. "No, I don't. It's none of my business." It seemed he'd said no more honestly spoken words since he'd arrived. If it hadn't been that someone had been looking for that damned silly picture collection, he might have given it up already. "That's not what concerns me."

"No? Don't want to ask pointed questions about my peculiar viewpoint? About my sex life? How I did my research? You show a remarkable amount of acceptance."

"Usually the public does accept these things well—or at least better than our friends and relatives. The public isn't as threatened by it. Someone close often feels it affects them directly. Of course, sometimes we manage to enrage both."

Roxanne stared at him a long time without answering. Then she did something unexpected. She took his hand, which had been lying on the table, and, raising his arm to rest on its elbow as if they were arm wrestling, pressed the flat of her hand against the flat of his. Bryce realized with shock that they were very nearly the same size. She seemed to be not so much comparing their dimensions as using this odd action as a display of understanding, even affection.

"What is it that you're investigating, exactly?" she asked quietly, lacing her fingers with his and unlacing them again.

"I'm interested in Taylor Adams. Specifically, I'm interested in his picture collection. Why would anyone want it, and where is it now?"

"I don't know the answer to either of those questions. Why does it concern you?"

"It makes me curious. Taylor was a bright boy, probably a natural manipulator, but emotionally, shall we say, very immature. Confused, even. And desperate. Very desperate. Now, I wonder, what had Taylor been up to the past year? He hadn't been on the street much . . . Was he preparing for his future? There's a rumor on the street he'd found himself a patron or patroness. . . . Was it you, Roxanne?"

"If you're asking me if I subsidized Taylor, I did not. He wasn't even paid for his modeling services."

Bryce looked at her sharply. She lightly touched the back of his knuckles, using her fingertips.

"Don't you believe me, Kevin?"

"I think tact runs in your family."

She raised an eyebrow, but he chose not to elaborate.

"It doesn't surprise me Taylor wasn't paid as a model. I suspect he didn't know he was one," he told her delicately.

She took a firmer hold of his hand, shifting it until he thought she actually might wrestle him.

"Once, when I was much younger and had just started writing," he said, "I had a discussion with a family friend, a psychology professor. She said something that I've thought about a lot over the years. We were talking about art in general—she seemed to think it applied to any art, whether it was writing or painting or sculpture. She stated—and I quote her exactly—'art has no ethics.' I've always wondered if that was true. Or if it was just that some artists have no ethics."

Her fingers moved down to lace themselves just below his wrists.

"What do you think, Roxanne?"

"I vote for narcissism," she said hoarsely. "Every time."

"I want to know why, Roxanne. I want to know why a damn silly lot of pictures a messed-up boy took is so important that someone would ransack two apartments looking for them. I want to know what it was that drove him off that bridge. I want to know if he really did it himself—or if someone helped him along." Bryce stopped to consider her tight grip. Her knuckles were white. "I want to know where that collection is and why it disappeared. And if whatever's occurred is over, or if there's more to come." It's what he wanted to know, but he wondered was it what Paul wanted to know.

Roxanne moved her hand again to press her palm against his.

"I don't know if Taylor was capable of love," he said. "I

don't know how much trust he could give, but my guess is, as much as he was capable of, he gave to you."

She sat back only slightly, so she would not be forced to let go of him as the waiter served espresso. They hadn't ordered it, the waiter had made a mistake. But they accepted his ministrations automatically. Roxanne stared at the steam curling from the cup, the sliver of lemon rind, and Bryce felt her attention slip away from him. He saw the smile play around the corners of her mouth, and he recognized the warning notes of aggravation. And maybe, also, he was simply tired of being nice.

"You know, when I first met you I thought I recognized something different in you—different from someone like Katharine. She puts on a cold face to the world, while you, on the surface, seem warm and hospitable. . . ." He continued softly, "But I think the real difference is something deeper than that. Scrape away Katharine's coolness, and you'll find warmth; under your warm surface there's nothing but ice."

He felt the hard pressure of her bony fingertips as they dug into his hand. Suddenly she let him go.

"I want to go home," she told him, and without any further hesitation, gathered her coat and went outside.

"Well, you wanted to see it, here it is," she said, and turned on the light.

This room was a long rectangle punctuated by arched windows, its walls gray as a cloudy day, a good background color for the few canvases hung there. Propped against the wall at the far end were more canvases, most stacked, but some separated from the others, all facing the wall. There was one plain wooden table, an easel, and shelves built into the wall for tools—paints, brushes, and assorted jars.

That half of the room represented work; and it was uncompromising.

The other half represented an equally spare version of pleasure. On a tightly woven rug in a purple so deep it was almost black, sat a white wicker dining set; two chairs, a pedestal with a glass top. Its location provided a comfortable view out a window with a bench padded in a cushion the same dark hue of the rug. Across it, a slash of white, was an afghan crocheted in a heavy, stiff material. Built into one corner was an old-fashioned cabinet; above it, on open shelves, he saw a stereo unit, tapes and records. Bryce wandered over to inspect. There were a few by the Police, but it was mostly jazz. Mixed into this sophisticated collection were a few diametrically opposed in style and content. Heavy metal rock and roll. Van Halen. Led Zeppelin. One or two other names unfamiliar to him but whose album covers left little doubt as to their content. It also left little doubt in his mind as to their ownership.

On the top shelf were two wineglasses and two brandy snifters flanking four books. One of his own, one appointment diary, one beautifully bound in green fabric, and a red leather-bound copy of Emile Zola's *Nana*. They were balanced against one another in the middle of the shelf, without bookends. The only frivolous note in the room was a large cone-shaped seashell; white and rough on the outside, pink and smooth on the inside. It served as a centerpiece on the wicker table.

"If you'd like something to drink, there's red wine or cognac in the cabinet," Roxanne told him.

A sampling of nearly all the really important physical pleasures in life, mused Bryce. Music, a good view, a comfortable place to sit, something to read, and something decent to drink. No doubt if you wanted your sense of smell satisfied, you could open the window and catch a whiff of the garden on the rooftop below or smell the tang of the sea. If you were cold, there was a blanket; if you wanted something beautiful to touch, there was the shell. This room held nothing superfluous.

"I don't need anything to drink, thank you," he called. She had come in no farther than the light switch. He reached for the green bound book and found it untitled. It also had a lock. Not a cheap diary lock, but an effective one. You couldn't jimmy this without leaving evidence. He put it back on the shelf.

"It's a little more extreme in this room," he remarked without looking at her. "It's as if in the other rooms, the ones you and Paul share, you made concessions to hospitality. In here you didn't bother." As he examined the tapes once more, he lightly touched the drawer. It was locked.

"No point in pleasing anyone but myself. It's rare to have anyone but me in here."

"Do you always lock the door to this room when you're not in?"

"Yes."

"Does anyone else have a key?"

"No."

"Not even Paul?"

"No."

He heard her close the door.

"Did Taylor have a key?"

He caught a glimpse of her out of the corner of his eye. Bracing herself against the closed door, she drove her hands down the front of her dress as if she were looking for pockets, a place to sling her hands. Bryce realized that must be exactly what she *was* doing. She was probably used to wearing a smock in this room, and this gesture was a habit.

"Yes," she said. Unhurriedly, she went on. "Paul has a place of his own. Taylor didn't."

"I see. That was very generous."

His tonelessness could have meant anything. Whatever it conveyed to her, it provoked the first flash of anger she had displayed for him. It was quick. It was spontaneous. And a second later it was gone.

"Yes, as a matter of fact, it was."

"Did he use it often?"

"Yes."

Casually, as if he were simply lounging, Bryce put his hands in his pockets. He submitted his next request respectfully.

"Do you mind if I look at your work? Or is that off limits?"

She grinned, suddenly teasing. "You mean you want to see my etchings?"

"Yes, I do."

She bowed slightly, drawing her arms in a wide circle, like an impressario.

"Be my guest. Once you enter the inner sanctum, all is open to you," she stated in mock drama.

"Thank you," he said, ignoring her levity.

He strolled like a lazy tourist through the working end of the room, stopping to flip methodically through each stack of canvases. Only two appeared to be finished works. One portrayed Roxanne with close cropped hair, wearing a man's business suit and holding a knife. She stood at the foot of a bed where a naked figure lay sprawled, face turned toward a wall. Body slit from throat to pelvis, its sex was obscured by the wound which had swelled and opened the body wide. The other painting was of a markedly different style. A canvas painted black, two figures crudely outlined in thick white paint, holding hands. The other hand of each figure held a gun; and was methodically blowing the heart from its partner. The heart was depicted as being literally thrown from the body. The rest were mostly sketches, ambiguous spots of color, phrases without a sentence. He bent down to examine the last one at some length. It seemed nearly finished. It showed a naked Roxanne, sitting crosslegged, matches scattered in the foreground, her body mutilated by burns. Even when he felt her hand on his shoulder, he didn't hurry. He got up slowly, pacing himself.

"You must think I'm some kind of monster," she said when they were eye to eye.

"Yes, I do," he stated. "But not because of what you painted, but because of the way I suspect you used your model."

"Is all this for some higher purpose or do you enjoy the company of monsters?"

"Of some, yes, I do." *I like seeing how close I can come to the edge before the ground gives way,* he thought dryly. From some distant room they could hear the phone ring. Her hand still lingered on his shoulder. "When was the last time Paul was in this room?"

"I don't know. Not for months."

"Has he been in here since Taylor died?"

"No." She opened her mouth as if to continue, then stopped herself.

"Not once, either with you or without you?"

"No."

The phone continued to ring.

"How was Taylor making his living, Roxanne?"

"I don't know. It wasn't something we discussed. I imagine he made it as he always had—only a little more discreetly."

"He never confided in you? Never told you of any big plans for his future?"

"*No!*" she exploded suddenly, gripping his arm. "That wasn't what he came here for!"

"What did he come here for?" he asked gently. "What could you two possibly have in common?"

She took her hand away and raised her chin.

"I think," he continued even more gently, "I have it figured out—at least, partially. My mind keeps returning to something I read once from van Gogh. He said, 'Being a laborer, I feel at home in the laboring class, and more and more I will try to live and take root there.' Shall I turn around that phrase and make it clearer, Roxanne?"

"Don't bother," she said shortly.

"Let's move on a little bit further. Gaugin's philosophy was to start painting from a still life and in the end dispense with the model—"

She turned abruptly, but he was quicker. He caught her and

spun her around, taking both shoulders in his hands, mindful that too much pressure might crush her.

"Roxanne, I'm not one of your in-laws. I'm going to view things a helluva lot differently than they do. You won't have to put up with anyone's unwanted sympathy or condescension."

She jerked her shoulders free. *Damn, I've fucked this thing up,* Bryce thought disgustedly as he watched her cross the room. *I've lost her.*

Roxanne had set her handbag on the table. She picked it up now and took a set of keys out. She held them out to Bryce.

"I want you to leave," she said, and there were tears in her eyes. "I don't want you to have to wait around for a taxi. Take my car."

Bryce made his way across the room, looking for a way to redeem the situation and finding none. He took the key ring and started for the door.

"Wait," she said.

He stopped. She went to the shelf drawing from it the locked book. She emptied a cassette box and two keys clattered out. Using one she opened the lock.

"You'll have to watch this. The catch slips into the lock easily, and if it does, you're out of luck because I'm not giving you the key. Everything I know is in here, and probably a lot you don't want to know. If you can keep the thing from locking, it's yours to read. If you don't . . ." She shrugged.

Bryce gazed at the book in his hand, pondering the flap with the catch. Then, as if he were simply shredding paper, he grabbed the flap and ripped it from the binding. He tossed it on the table.

With that, he made his exit.

Chapter Eleven

■

The phone was ringing in Bryce's hotel room. He could hear it through the door, and as he jammed the key into the lock, he thought he might not get to it in time. When he finally made it into the room, he was sure it was on its last ring.

"Hello," he said breathlessly.

"Good morning."

"Good evening," he countered. Katharine's voice always sounded huskier over the phone. He threw the book and his key on the bed and flopped down beside them. He began to unbutton the shirt under his pullover sweater.

"I suppose it still must be over there," she said doubtfully. "But not by much. Were you out?"

You know I was. You must have called before. Bryce grinned into the receiver. "Yes. I had dinner with Roxanne."

"Oh? How do you like her?"

"She reminds me of a diamond. Cold, with a lot of sharp points, and absolutely beautiful."

Katharine said nothing. For a moment Bryce thought they'd been disconnected.

"Hello?"

"So you're not bored? Getting caught up in what you're doing?"

"I've got the feeling it's going to be messy," Bryce told her.

"Well, that should be good for you, shouldn't it? It will make your mind all bright and keen again."

"Katharine, you little pain in the ass, are you telling me I was getting dull?"

She laughed, and if listening to her talk over the phone was good, listening to her laugh was even better.

"You were getting cranky."

Bryce made some small, indistinct sound of disgust, and she laughed again. When her laughter faded, he sensed her hesitation.

"It's so stupid," she said finally. "I thought of all kinds of things to tell you before, and now that I'm on the phone, I can't think of one of them."

How about "I love you?" That's a good start. Even I have been known to mumble it when we're making love and I've had too much to drink.

Instead, he said, "Are you all right there by yourself? No catastrophes other than your cooking?"

"Oh, fine. James came back, so he's been sleeping with me."

"*What?*"

"James," she continued in her calm way, attributing his response to a hearing problem rather than to the economy of her phrasing. "I think he wanted an excuse to leave London, and I was it. He installed himself outside the bedroom door, saying he was going to protect me from the ravages of God only knows what—the IRA, the RUC, the British Army—*something*. He's been entertaining me with his usual nonsense."

"Still camped *outside* the bedroom door?" he questioned,

knowing he was being silly, partly aggravated at himself, partly laughing.

"No, I've convinced him the sofa would do just as well. He's at home on it now, recovering from breakfast. I tried to convince him not to try my coffee cake, but he insisted on being heroic. Brave man."

"Foolhardy is more like it," Bryce said, and though they couldn't see one another, they both smiled, each knowing that the other was.

"That sort of thing usually goes hand in hand," she said, and went on in a rush, "Kevin, I . . ."

Come on, he coached. *Say it, Katharine. Say* it. It's simple. Three words. Go on. I'll *believe* you.

". . . miss you."

You miss me. That's very good. That's progress. Was it because there was no warm body on which to toast her cold feet? No one to cook something edible? No convenient stud service for the child she wanted so badly?

"I miss you too," he said. "They don't supply electric blankets here."

There was an awkward silence, and during its short span the realization that he was exhausted swept over him. He sighed heavily.

"Tired?" she asked.

"Yes."

"I should let you go, then. Do me a favor, will you? If you can."

"Anything you like," he drawled.

"Don't be angry with me—for getting you into this."

"Actually, it's rather challenging. I think I'm beginning to enjoy it," he confessed, as much to himself as to her.

"Terrific," she said, and Bryce wondered if he just imagined a hint of dryness in her tone. But her next words sounded sincere. "I'm glad."

They dawdled over a few more sentences. When they finally

hung up, Bryce lay back on the bed, arms thrown over his head, one knee bent up slightly, his sweater halfway up his chest, rumpled from where he had dug under it. Talking to Katharine left him both pleased and exasperated. He thought of Roxanne and wondered if she had ever loved anyone in her life. He thought of himself and wondered why the things you needed always seemed to come late. Idly, he picked up the book next to him and began to read.

Chapter Twelve

▪

For some time I've felt San Francisco has exhausted its possibilities for me. I've been here almost ten years—longer than I have lived anywhere. I want to see something new to refresh my perspective. How can one improve and broaden their work unless they do? My interest has settled on the Middle East. Cairo, Kuwait, Tel Aviv, cities growing out of the desert. I want to see the juxtaposition of new and old, the people caught in between. I talked to a director of the Academy of Art, a woman with a certain amount of influence. Late one afternoon she gave me a call. . . .

Paul was the first one I rushed to. I could hardly wait for him to get home—would even have met him at the office, except I was sure he'd already left. He had no more than one foot in the door when I was blurting out the whole story. Afterward, I watched him at the bar, fixing himself a club soda, and wondered at his silence.

"How long is the position for?" he asked me finally.

"Only a year. I'd spend a certain amount of time doing technical drawing for an archeological group from U.C. Berkeley, but there would be time for my own work—with a group like that, I'd get the opportunity to see a real cross-section—"

"Only *a year?" Paul's question was sharp.* "Only*?"*

I hesitated, sensing the danger.

"I can't take a year off of work right now," Paul pointed out.

I'd never considered Paul joining me. "I know—" I started.

"Oh? You do?" I had greatly underestimated this situation. Paul pulled back the flaps of his suitcoat and was gripping his hips with his hands as he came around the bar.

"I told you before, Rox. When you mentioned the idea of the Middle East, I said I'd take you. Next year or the year after I could take a whole month—"

"A month isn't good enough—"

"Why the hell not? *Do what you can in a month. Rox, those people are nuts over there. They blow up babies, trees, buildings, whole communities—"*

"A month isn't good enough," I repeated more forcefully. I wanted him to understand my point of view—it was so necessary and reasonable for me to go. "And what am I supposed to do for two years, Paul? Sit around and twiddle my thumbs? I can't wait that long. I just happened to hit it lucky that the scheduled artist—"

"You can't or you won't*?" Paul was looking at me, sizing up the situation. I looked away, and he saw more in that simple action than I intended.*

"You want to go away, don't you," he said. It wasn't a question. "You don't want me around." He was caught between disbelief and pure rage. "After all, I make life so miserable for you. I give you everything you want and do everything possible to ensure that you can continue working—"

"Paul, I'm not complaining." In my exasperation, I nearly wailed. "You've been wonderful."

"But it isn't enough, is it? Because you want to go, Rox, and you want to go without me." He said it with a blank expression on his face I found chilling. "I'm screwed any way I go. If I keep you here, you're going to resent it—if you go, then I'm stuck alone." With every word, he grew louder and more intense. "You're my wife."

"It's only a year," I asserted feebly. "I'll write, I'll call, I'll be back."

Paul examined my face so minutely it seemed he was memorizing every line, every pore. "Will you? I'm not so sure. Can you promise that?"

But I don't like to make promises. I realized my hands were stuck in the pockets of the expensive jeans I wore, my focus on my paint-spattered shoes.

"I won't let myself be used, Roxanne. Maybe you have more of me than you want because you can't come and go. You stay or you go. I don't know anything in between."

"It's only—"

"Now, *it's only a year. But I know you, Rox. Once it starts, it will snowball," he said tiredly. He started for the hall but stopped quite near and made his final analysis in a voice barely above a whisper: "I can't get over that you want to leave me. What would I do without you?"*

I ran. I got into my car and headed toward the Golden Gate Bridge with some ridiculous idea of driving to Marin. But I already felt a rigor mortis taking hold of me, starting on the inside, working its way out. I drove to the Marina. Coming into the parking lot, I passed a car going out that looked a lot like Rob's, but I quickly turned my face away. The last thing I wanted was to converse with a member of Paul's family, even Rob. The car sped by.

I parked facing the bay and tried to imagine life without Paul. Gripping the steering wheel, my hands were white. The colors of the bay, of Alcatraz Island, were swirled and blurred as if done by the hand of a melancholy impressionist. I concentrated on these imaginary brush strokes, following their curvy trails, their splotches of dismal color. . .

The passenger door opened suddenly, and in much the same way Taylor flopped onto my wet slicker, he landed in the front seat of my car. Grinning, mischievous, expecting to be welcomed with open arms. I gaped at him, my hands clamped to the wheel. My vision cleared and blurred while tears slid down my face, rolled off my chin.

In an instant of clear sight I saw panic in Taylor. In another second he would thrash his way out of the car and run. When my vision blurred again, I waited for the slam of the car door.

Instead I felt his hands on my face. They touched me gently, brushing aside the wetness, but their texture was rough like a chamois cloth that has become stiff in spots from contact with material too rough for it. He was mumbling, and my mind was too cluttered to understand a word he said.

My face in both his hands, Taylor leaned in my direction. I wanted to touch him, to put my hands in his hair, but I waited. His breath was warm, his mouth probably flavored with the sweet, pungent taste of tobacco. His hands moved down my neck, under my hair, as if he was afraid I might slip away.

The outside mirror, bent at an odd angle, peered in toward us instead of out toward the street. Taylor caught sight of himself and hesitated; suddenly, he let me go. He fell back in the seat, head bent back on the headrest.

"I'm moving," he said. "Can you give me a lift?"

We were in a small room in an apartment on the far end of California Street. Taylor was throwing clothes into a suitcase. There was a bed, a nightstand, a stereo unit, posters on the wall, records strewn over the floor. But what captured my attention were the picture frames. Rows and rows of them lined up on shelves, windowsills, on the nightstand. Lovely frames, chosen with much more care than he had ever picked his friends or lovers. The photographs—people smiling, hugging, holding fishing poles. There were two of Paul's family motor sailer.

I have a life, it is recorded in Kodak print.

He packed all his frames and photos carefully into a separate box.

That was all he took—his clothes, his photos, a few records. I drove him to a North Beach address. I didn't bother to take note of it—I knew he wouldn't be there long.

That was when I gave him the key to my studio.

To my surprise, Taylor used the studio. He installed his favorite records—thank God for earphones!—and even a few photographs. He usually stopped by in the late afternoon, rarely disturbing my own worktime since I paint best in the early morning. Sometimes Taylor shared a cocktail with Paul and me after Paul got home. But his attitude toward Paul seemed to have changed. He still had the touch of awe for him, but now I caught Taylor almost glaring at Paul when he thought no one was looking, and there was a stiffness to him that I'd never noticed before. Usually he left before Paul came home.

Even toward me he was different. I'd touch him innocently, even accidentally, and he'd jump away. Yet he always stayed near, just out of reach.

And there was a new tenseness in me. Day after day I'd sit in my studio, staring at my canvases. Paul would ask me about my trip and I'd never answer. I thought he would force the issue, but then, surprisingly, he let it go.

I sat at my table, executing mindless sketches. Over and over, week upon week, they piled up, a veritable stockpile of nothingness, a collection of wasted time.

One day, for novelty, I took these doodles and lined them across the floor of my studio. They covered the whole floor except for one single, slender footpath through the center. I walked up and down the path, hands clenched behind my back, like a schoolmarm viewing a group of errant pupils, ones in need of relentlessly harsh discipline.

As I considered them I saw a pattern emerge. With mounting excitement, I quickly regrouped the studies according to subject matter, in chronological order—times of day, sequence of events.

Early morning. Deliveries of bread and produce to groceries, restaurants. A few bums, casualties left from the night before. The migration of workers to their jobs; shop workers setting up their outside displays, florists with vivid tubs of flowers, an old, weathered Italian man setting up a table of apples and oranges in front of his grocery, its windows decorated with hand-lettered signs announcing the day's specials. The old man waves his hand, greeting a restauranteur across the street, who doesn't see him. Well-dressed business people stop for croissants and coffee in a small shop, newspapers propped on coffee cups.

Midday. The lunch crowd, everyone vying for nourishment at fast-food outlets, at corner restaurants. Everyone in a hurry for service, demanding their due. The afternoon shoppers, bookstore clientele, eyes averted to scrutinize volumes. Men with close-cropped hair and beards move in and out of gyms, duffel bags in hand, walking as if there were a rod stuck through their rectum, up their spine.

Mid-afternoon. Teenagers take over more of the street. A young boy here and there. Another. And another. They collect, magnetized to certain gathering spots. Young girls walk by, teasing, swaying their hips. A cluster of youngsters worshipfully surround the video game at a corner grocery.

Women, eyes focused on the next step, walk from their jobs to the bus stops, the cable cars, to home. The street becomes crowded with people rushing to and from. Business in the bars begins to pick up, daylight dims. The Italian man puts away his oranges, the florist brings in his last bedraggled bunches of flowers, the street begins to display other goods. . . .

* * *

Weeks later I was surrounded by painted canvases. On its own, each work was interesting. Lined up side by side, they told a story—exposed a progression.

But it was an incomplete story. It was like telling the tale of Little Red Riding Hood and not showing the wolf in Grandmother's bed.

Taylor never looked at my work. He'd sit on the window seat or lie on the rug, headphones on his ears, listening to records. And dreamed, I suppose.

At first I resisted the idea of taking the series a step further. But a look at Taylor and his surface was exactly what I needed. The contrast between bravado and truth, the war between what we desire and what is possible, could have been achieved so easily; the outline was there, waiting to be played upon.

His was a face used to playing parts, and he did them so well, it was possible to believe them. When I gave him some off-hand compliment and he reddened, his eyes moved away and he smiled—I'd almost think he was genuinely touched. When he brought me a flower or bought me dinner, I almost believed it a sincere gesture. When Paul sat next to me, put his arm on my shoulder and I saw Taylor clench his glass and stare at his shoes, I almost imagined I saw jealousy.

But it was Taylor's business to provide illusions—no, more than business, his way of life. I always took that into account.

I would have liked to believe one of Taylor's surfaces was real. The more I thought about it, the more obsessed I became. I wanted to touch him, but he wouldn't let me. So strongly did I identify with him, I almost felt we were already attached in some physical way. That he was mine to do with as I would, designed for my purpose.

But that's absurd, I told myself.

* * *

It was night. My car was in the shop with some awful pinging noise. I'd borrowed Rob's while Paul and he did something rare—they went to a football game. I'd been shopping in Union Square—Christmas presents for Paul. I did what had by now become habit. I drove down Polk on the way home, past the noisy section, at the quiet end populated with nice restaurants and apartment buildings, antique shops. There's a store that carries safari clothes, odd hats and shoes. It's open late for the holidays, and on impulse I stopped. Rob has always enjoyed hats, and I thought that for Christmas I'd add another to his collection.

Inside, I wandered through the exotic African displays, picking up articles of clothing only to put them down again. I paused near the storefront, and glancing out the window, saw Taylor across the street. I was about to go outside and call to him when something stopped me.

He was walking with the determined set of someone with a specific destination in mind. He slowed momentarily next to Rob's car, looking at it, then over his shoulder. Why? I wondered. Under a streetlight he checked his watch. Was he meeting someone? He turned, walking backward, examining where he'd just been. He spun forward, scanning the street. Evidently he was, what? Disappointed? Worried? Disturbed? I could see him frowning. He looked at his watch again. Was he late? Early? For what? He stopped. I almost thought he was going to start walking toward the car again; he took a step in that direction, and on his face I saw confusion. His face looked very natural in a state of confusion, oddly lovable.

He spun around abruptly. Had someone called his name? Yes. Even in the light provided, framed as he was by the arch of the apartment-building doorway, the newcomer looked like a dark angel, sinister and not quite real. Skin the color of caramel, a tautness to his stance even loose and bulky clothes could not hide, the arrogance, the cool evil of the supremely indifferent.

In a few quick steps Taylor slid into the dark then into the light of the doorway with him. They were talking, and the dark man's head jerked toward the inside of the stairwell. Taylor shrugged, and looked away with an expression I'd never seen on his face before.

I strained forward to see.

Were they angry? It was hard to tell. The dark man stood a step above Taylor on the stairs, took another step, and the darkness of his clothes merged with the shadows of the hall. Only his face was in the light. He stood as if that was all there was of him: a cold face suspended in mid-air. Taylor struggled to appear disinterested, but the mouth of the dark man was moving. And Taylor was listening. The man disappeared, and Taylor took one last look around before following him, shoulders slumped, hands hidden in his jacket pockets.

I moved to the restaurant next door. I sat. And stared. And waited.

Bryce got up to use the bathroom.

In some ways, he could almost have written this journal himself; articulated the reluctance, then the sense of urgency that would drive her on. After all, why did just James's name appear on their joint work? Wasn't he afraid of what a small, select audience might read, even through the distortions of his craft, and perhaps misunderstand? There were certain responsibilities Bryce had taken very seriously, feelings he had wanted to protect at all costs.

The way Roxanne wrote, particularly of her childhood, as if holding her past at arm's length, left him with a disquieting sense of watching the lame struggling to walk, of being unable to offer help without giving offense. For he was convinced Roxanne was a cripple. One whose need for self-protection, whose capability for self-delusion, destroyed everyone around her, for she had such powerful weapons.

He suddenly realized that he was staring at his own reflection in the bathroom mirror; looking carefully, seeing nothing. Katharine had told him his eyes were hazel, that sometimes they'd change. To what? he wondered. And when? And why? (They appeared a little green now. So green must be one of his colors.) But he knew as soon as he stepped away from this mirror he'd forget all about these unimportant questions. And somehow he was afraid that was what Roxanne would do with her private self-analysis. Having once written it, might walk away and forget.

Bryce was also afraid that Roxanne was right. If this was the crime he thought it was, it couldn't be prosecuted. He went back to bed to read.

Chapter Thirteen

▪

The decision had been made for me. Opportunity had been so easily provided, it seemed more like an edict than a temptation. In all the time I'd driven in the area, this was the first time I'd ever seen Taylor here. But I'd seen the dark young man. And my guess was, if I timed it right, he wouldn't be hard to find.

It took me less than a week to arrange. Paul had a late meeting. Taylor was modeling again at the Academy. I knew he'd be there until at least seven o'clock. In fact, I called to make sure, and arranged to meet him at seven-thirty for dinner. That gave me an hour and a half—between five-thirty and seven—to do what I had to do.

I dressed conservatively, black silk with gray pinstripes, because I wanted to be taken seriously—I wanted respect. Expensively, because people always give extra attention to the well-dressed, particularly in business details. I wore no jewelry—why tempt him to rob me? And brought no more cash than I thought I'd need, even though I wasn't sure exactly how much that was. In the end it didn't matter anyway, because I didn't need it.

I found him leaning outside an old block building, his hands in his jacket pockets, one heel braced in the seam of mortar between the rocks. He might have been fifteen. He might have been twenty-five. With a little rearrangement he might even have been female. As I stood in front of him, he planted both feet on the ground, taller than I expected. I drew myself up straight and put my hands deep in the pockets of my silk. My approach was direct. I did not know any other way.

"I just want an hour or so of your time. You'll get whatever is your usual compensation."

He looked at me, and in a situation in which most boys on the street might have harassed me or been lewd, he just stared. Although he didn't move, I could have sworn he shrugged. I told him where I wanted to go, and sensed that behind that ambiguous mask, his interest quickened.

It wasn't long before I found myself in the room that would provide the background I needed. I walked in, listening for his movements behind me. I wanted always to be aware of where he was—of what he was doing. He closed the door softly and leaned against it, taking much the same stance he had on the street. Taking a notebook from my pocket, I made some quick sketches. There was a large mirror, a bed, a dresser, a tiny bathroom, an alcove. I went to the alcove and pulled the drapes, standing there as I had seen Taylor do that night, even imitating his positions, seeing things from his view. Below there was the little restaurant with its blue curtain, the street traffic, and the Italian man bringing his oranges back into the store as daylight faded. I heard the boy shuffle behind me and I turned. He was staring at the floor, but I had the impression that his gaze had been diverted there only when he'd drawn my attention. I turned back to the window and saw the old man locking the door to his grocery. He stared up at my window and I smiled at him.

"Do you live here?" I asked the boy behind me.

"No," he answered. He had a quiet voice, a liquid contralto that could have lulled me to sleep.

I crossed the room, my high heels clicking on the exposed floor between the small rugs scattered there. I had an impulse to walk on tiptoe but restrained it. I opened a chest of drawers below the mirror. In it were some of the utensils of the trade. I didn't know all their names or uses, and although my companion could have provided me with answers, I didn't bother to ask. It wasn't important. What was *important was that I understood their shape and texture.*

I closed the drawer, and in the mirror saw him watching my reflection. God, he was beautiful. Different from Taylor. Colder. Yet I wondered what it would be like to touch him, just like I wondered what it would be like to touch Taylor. I tried to imagine it. But what I saw was his leaning against the door, his arms folded, his features no more than a dark creaminess set above a faun's physique. My hair was pulled back, and in the mirror my own features became skeletal. The instruments I'd handled danced above my head teasingly.

"Do you want to watch?" I heard him say, though I couldn't see his lips move. "It could be arranged."

"No," I answered, and my teeth were sharp and pointed in that bony frame. I tried to refocus, but it was hard. I kept seeing us like a surrealist vision I would have never painted myself. And I was drawn to it, unsure whether it was a warning, a premonition, an exposé, or all three. Slowly, I drew the pins from my hair, letting it fall, hoping its fullness would change the image, put flesh back onto my bones.

I focused. He was again a beautiful young man staring at a woman whose motives he would not understand. I moved toward him, less businesslike now than on the street.

"Satisfied?" he asked.

A funny way to put it, but yes, I was satisfied. Excited. Confused. I stared at him and knew I identified as much with this boy's arrogance as I did with Taylor's self-hatred. When I answered, I was as cool as he.

He straightened, and again I was surprised by his height. He was a slim man. From a distance he seemed almost delicate. Up close he was no more delicate than an iron rod. But at that moment I felt whatever hardness he had, I could match. Usually, I prefer my paints, the thought to the actual deed. It's more sensual, free from the contamination of someone else's expectations. But I never supposed this man had much in the way of expectations, even less in the way of illusions. He was incapable of being surprised. He looked at me as if he were looking into a mirror. I touched the collar of his jacket and felt extraordinarily alert. Each button he pulled open on the front of my dress flared my curiosity, my hunger for success. As he pushed his mouth on mine, picked me up and pressed my back to a wall, that hunger reached for him as if I could obtain from him the fuel I'd need to get me through the next few weeks.

For some odd reason, I felt right at home in this room.

Six months later the exhibit opened to somewhat astonished reviews, accusing me of everything from penis envy to some special God-given understanding of human frailty. I didn't pay any attention. Reviewing is a critic's business, not mine. But I did feel very satisfied with what I'd done. I'd go to the gallery to see it—just to relive that sense of purpose. Painting can be demanding, tedious work, but my concentration had never been stronger than when I'd worked on that last series. It blocked all else from my mind, and it was a pleasure to live off that euphoria for a while. I knew soon enough it would be forgotten, as if I'd never painted the series. Just as when you're hungry you forget the sensation of fullness, soon I would be starving for something new.

* * *

I wasn't there the afternoon Taylor walked into the gallery. Taylor seeing the exhibit was something I hadn't considered. He'd never been interested in art, per se, not even mine. He liked modeling for the Academy because of the attention—I don't think he ever once looked at the canvases. Perhaps I hadn't wanted to consider the possibility, for if I had, I might not have done the series, and deep down I rejected that alternative.

I don't know where he heard about the show, he never told me. I'd never mentioned it to him. He hadn't modeled for the Academy since Christmastime—so it wasn't there. In fact, he had told me he wasn't going to model for them anymore—though he gave me no reasons.

The gallery owner recognized him in spite of the mirrored sunglasses and cap he wore. Later, he carefully detailed to me how he watched Taylor as he started through the "Day Scenes" section with what seemed to be an almost disinterested air. How even the "Transitions" section didn't seem to inspire any special display of attention.

But as Taylor neared "Views from a Window" and saw the painting of the old grocer putting away his produce, he stopped. From there on he distanced himself as he passed frame after frame, a little farther from the paintings. The muscles on his face twitched, like the sudden movement of a sculptor chiseling off a flick of stone; I can imagine the paintings mirrored in the lens of his glasses until he stopped to stare motionless at the gaping space of a sold painting.

When Taylor burst into the studio, I had no idea what was wrong. It was four-thirty exactly. I know because I was staring at my watch as I tried to compose a letter to my agent, who was arranging for the paintings to be exhibited in New York. Suddenly Taylor was there.

I hate sunglasses. I hate the way they make it impossible to read someone, the way they conceal information. But I didn't need to see Taylor's eyes to know something was terribly wrong. It was detailed in every straight and rigid muscle, in the skin sunk under his already prominent cheekbones, the way his arms ended in fists that appeared to be no more than white and red blotched stubs.

Instinctively I stood and backed away, jostling my coffee cup, staining the letter beside it. I knew at once that whatever terror was on his mind was directed toward me. I kept staring at those great black mirrors where his eyes should have been, and all I saw was me.

"I was just down on Sutter," he told me in a voice I wouldn't have recognized if I hadn't seen him speaking. "Why?" *he asked.*

I shoved my hands down my smock, later discovering I'd ripped a hole right through the seam of the pocket. I murmured some inadequate explanation to the effect that it was how I saw it, and his fist came down so hard on the glass-top table, I was surprised it didn't crack.

"Why me? *Why not someone else?" He rammed his fingers through his hair, knocking his cap off without being aware of it.*

"Because that's how it was—because you were perfect," I said, and he looked at me as if I were out of my mind. He sat down in the chair I'd been sitting in and rocked back and forth as if his stomach hurt.

"How the hell did you know*?" he said, and I could see I'd destroyed every image he had about the way he presented himself.*

"I was told long before I even met you." But he wasn't listening, he just kept rocking. "They were only pictures, *for Chrissake," I told him, and he stopped rocking and looked at me. I thought he was going to get up and hit me.*

But he didn't. He took off his glasses and laid them tiredly on the table. His eyes were pink, red-rimmed, and wet. I hadn't seen a man cry since my father, and I'd forgotten that until this moment. How devastating it was, the awful compulsion one felt to stop it at any cost. He hid his face in his hands and a tremor ran up his back.

The next thing I knew, I was kneeling at his feet, holding him, and he wasn't resisting. I'd never felt anything as hot as his body. "They're only pictures," I mumbled feebly over and over. "They don't matter. None of it does." I kept holding him as if to transfer his pain to me; then I could forget it, like I did everything else.

But pictures were an important part of his life. I should have known that. It was one thing I should have understood completely.

We sat there for a while before he took his arms away, reluctantly. Then he slowly emptied his pockets, stopping now and then to take a small, shaky suck for air or to sniffle. There was something too weary and hopeless about it to remind me of the recovery of a child from a crying jag. It was as if Taylor had suddenly grown up—or simply gotten old.

He arranged his possessions in piles. Wallet, keys, sunglasses case, ticket stubs, even change. Tidy piles of coin arranged according to denomination. It was a curious ritual, maybe something he had seen in a movie. He didn't look at me, though my arms hugged his knees. After he was through, he touched my hair.

"I love you," he said hoarsely. "I know you don't believe that, but I do."

I thought he'd suddenly kicked me in the stomach. But it was just my own physical reaction. I tried to explain how he and I and the pictures were mixed in such an oddly tangled way; exposing more of me than of him. But he didn't understand a word. I don't think he was even listening. I finally just shut up, and he sat above me, shaking his head.

He had a hard time pushing me away because I didn't want to let go. I thought if I held on long enough, hard enough, I could make it pass.

But Taylor was equally determined, and a lot stronger than me. With an effort he broke my hold and stood me up, giving that odd sort of laugh men use when they can't quite believe what they see, like a play in a football game they find completely unfathomable.

"Roxanne," he said. Whoever he was playing now, he was doing it well. He nodded to the things on the table. "This is everything I have. It's yours. Keep it for me. Do you understand?"

I didn't understand, but I didn't question him. I was trembling. He stepped away and put his hands on his hips in a way that reminded me of Paul.

"Where did you meet the Angel?"

I didn't know what he meant. He must have been talking nonsense.

"The Angel," he repeated. "Jesus. You might as well tell me."

But I didn't know what he wanted. I would have told him anything, given him anything.

He swore. He was getting agitated again. "Shit," he said, "I guess it doesn't matter anyway." He backed up to the wall, using it to prop up his body, banging the back of his head against it four or five times, hard.

I started toward him. I think I was saying his name, but he put his hands up.

"You've got everything, lady. I don't have any more for anyone to take." He was rolling his head back and forth against the wall. "This world's too complicated for me." He laughed, but it was a threadbare sort of sound and it scared me. I turned my head away. But that couldn't hide the evidence of how I'd failed someone I'd loved, couldn't keep me from seeing yet another's passions exceeding what I'd expected, skyrocketing out of my control.

I heard him say my name. By the time I'd turned, he had gone.

* * *

Paul read about his death in the papers. He tried to break it to me gently, but he needn't have bothered. The news didn't come as a surprise.

That night I made love to Paul more fiercely than I ever had, thinking I might feel some spark that would prove to me I really was still alive.

But I didn't.

I lie in bed at night, or sit in my studio in the afternoon in front of a blank canvas that usually seems to stay blank. I try to analyze everything. I can see how easy it is to make this progression, from liar to whore to murderess. It seems a natural progression. I should have never taken the first step. I don't know how many times I've wished I could have taken Taylor and Paul and molded them into one man: the spontaneity I felt for one, the respect I felt for the other. But that is not possible. What is terrifying is that it might not have made any difference anyway.

But as much as I examine, there are some things I don't understand. Why did Taylor have to take my pictures so seriously? Why does Paul have to take my leaving so seriously? Paintings are only pigment on canvas. I'm only a woman—and not an especially good one, at that. Why can't I change it all with one bold stroke?

I never wanted to hurt anyone.

The phone with its furious insistence penetrated his sleep. It's Katharine, he thought, phoning back to tell me everything I want to hear. He even whispered her name into the receiver.

"Kevin?" The voice brought him to his senses.

"Angelo?"

"You got it right this time."

"What is it?"

"Got something I think you'll be interested in."

"Such as?"

Angelo paused to speak to one of his subordinates, his message muffled. Suddenly he was talking to Bryce again, his voice sharp and ungodly energetic for that time of the morning.

"A dead body. One of yours, I think. And no suicide this time. You wanna get your ass out of bed?"

Chapter Fourteen

■

"Bacon and eggs."

"Cheese omelet," Angelo said.

They handed their menus back to a young man with a face as broad and friendly as a Nebraska farm boy's. An old woman's heavily accented voice called out orders at a pitch that made Bryce wince and then grin. Wide window panels took up two walls of the small diner, and he stared out at the waves, which rolled toward the ruins of the old Sutro baths below, barely perceptible through a heavy mist that would soon lift into rain. Angelo's voice droned in his ear.

"Stability," he was lecturing. "There isn't enough of it in this world—especially this part of the world. That's why I like this place," he said, grasping his coffee cup and nodding ambiguously in the direction of the restaurant's center aisle. "Been here close to fifty years. See that old lady over there? She's been working here over thirty-five years." He gave the table two light raps with his knuckles. "Thirty-five years. Ever since she emigrated."

"From where?" Bryce asked. He had been trying to place the accent.

Angelo shrugged. "Russia, I think. But she must have knocked around a bit. I haven't heard anyone come in here yet with a language she couldn't speak."

Bryce tried to guess her age, wondering where she might have been during World War II; trying to get a sense of her place in history.

"Stability," Angelo went on. "Fifty years in the same location—that's stability, thirty-five working at the same job—that's stability." He leaned forward. "Do you know they put Velveeta in their cheese omelets? None of that natural shit. Good old American junk food—like mother used to make," he said seriously. "Probably started using Velveeta the year it came out—that's stability." He finished with the air of a lawyer who had just made an indisputable point.

Bryce looked at Angelo, who lit a cigarette. Junk food, junk stability, Bryce thought. In the end you had to place your faith in people—which brought him to the problem at hand.

"How long had he been dead?"

Angelo sighed, letting Bryce know that he had been hoping to enjoy a breakfast unsullied by the details of work. Bryce gazed at him unblinkingly, and Angelo gave a fatalistic flutter of his hands that spread ash over the Formica-topped table.

"About three hours, that's the educated guess. That Gautier—what's his first name? Peter? Paul? Paul Gautier. Said he came in, found him, and called us right away."

"Anybody see him arrive?"

"Gautier, you mean? Yeah, as a matter of fact it was one of us. That parking lot is patrolled pretty regularly. One of our cars cruised by just as he pulled up. It was the nearest patrol car when the dispatcher called, and the first on the scene. Whole thing took less than five minutes."

Bryce drew an invisible pattern on the tabletop with the blunt end of his fork, and drank some coffee. He glanced up briefly at

Angelo, as if to signal him to continue, and Angelo did so as if Bryce was still his superior.

"Arrived at around eleven o'clock. I waited to call you until we got some of the facts put together. Don't suppose you want to be bothered with that bullshit work anymore—let you sleep a bit," Angelo said, without any particular show of consideration in his voice.

"What made you think this case would be of interest to me?"

Angelo looked injured. "What am I? A fucking *idiot*? I can put two and two together and come up with four. Listen, I saw those paintings. After Taylor died, I went partly out of curiosity and partly as a . . . tribute. Yeah, that's the word. Tribute. Taylor was something to remember. I also remember the name of the artist—read the bulletin on her. Gautier. A woman's name. I have you snooping around asking about Taylor, and now it seems we have a dead relative on the family boat. Maybe this is a family matter too? Family matters sometimes get messy."

"Sometimes they do."

"So," Angelo went on, "I figure I got a busy work schedule. Could always use an extra hand. Could be there's some interesting and surprising things floating around in your head."

Bryce considered Angelo expressionlessly.

Angelo nodded without smiling. "Thought so," he said.

"Can you give me a description of the victim?" Bryce asked.

"Yeah. Cut to ribbons."

The waiter was in the act of delivering their breakfast, but seemed no more startled than if Angelo had said good morning. He gave them a broad, congenial smile.

"A slightly more detailed description, please," Bryce prodded as he put salt and pepper on his eggs and the man left them.

"Male. Aged twenty-eight. Height about five eight. Weight possibly around 175—he was a little pudgy. Dark hair. Naked.

Stabbed. Hit over the head with a blunt instrument. Namely, a small fire extinguisher. Had a welt the size of a fist under his left eye.'' Angelo cut into his omelet and took a bite before continuing. ''His name was Robin Gautier. Brother of Paul and son of George, who both happen to be listed on the boat's registration. No sign of forced entry. Nothing stolen, so far as anyone can tell. The place was torn apart. Suspect sexual activity—specifically, homosexual activity—before he hit the big one.''

Bryce mashed his eggs into his potatoes.

''So,'' Angelo said, ''this situation brings up some interesting questions. I was thinking someone has got to be looking for something specific. Drugs, maybe? Did they find it? What's this Gautier family like?''

''Very respectable,'' Bryce said. ''Hearth, home, and old-fashioned values.''

''Then my guess is we have an old-fashioned black sheep here.''

''Possibly.''

They concentrated on breakfast. Outside, gulls flew low near the window; far below, sitting on a skeleton of an old pool, a squirrel sat bolt upright looking out to sea. Bryce's gaze drifted up toward the twisted cypresses poised on the cliff's edge, swept up from the sea in a manicured curve, before he turned to Angelo, who was spooning his meal into his mouth, eating almost as rapidly as he spoke.

''Did Paul give any reason for being at the harbor?'' Bryce asked. Angelo stopped eating to look at him. ''Eleven o'clock at night seems like an odd time to go sailing.'' Especially, Bryce thought, if you're supposed to be going out of town. Roxanne had never been specific as to where he was going that night or how he was going to get there, but somehow her wording didn't tally with a sailing trip. And then there was the matter of the weather, not exactly the best of conditions on the bay.

''It's his boat, he can twiddle around it any time, day or night. But I thought it was a little unusual myself. So I asked. Said he just had a fight with his wife and came to the boat to think. It's quiet and usually stocked with a bottle of Chivas Regal. Sounds reasonable. When I had a wife, I was fighting with her too. Needed a bottle of Chivas Regal."

Bryce put his elbows on the table and dropped his wadded napkin on his plate. He leaned back in his seat, arms crossed in front of him.

"One brother uses the place to run from his wife, the other to hole up with his boyfriends. Cozy. Funny they've never run into one another before," Angelo said, keeping his eyes focused on his knife.

"Paul didn't know his brother was gay?" Bryce asked.

"Did not appear so. Or at least he didn't know he was using the boat for his pickups." Angelo licked butter off his thumb. "Of course, maybe that's what we have here. Guy out for a little affection brings home something kinkier than he expected. It happens." Angelo pursed his lips. "So what do you think? Is that what we have here?"

Bryce was slow to answer, but when he did, he did so with decision.

"Paul was lying on one point. He didn't argue with his wife last night."

"Oh?"

"No. He couldn't have. His wife was with me."

Angelo arched his eyebrows. "That might be a good reason to have an argument."

"Possibly," Bryce replied, "but the fact is, he had no opportunity. I didn't leave her until after eleven."

"I see," said Angelo, and followed that dry comment with a "well, well, well," that could have been meant for Bryce or Paul or both.

"He was supposed to be going out of town for a couple of days," Bryce amended crisply.

Angelo discarded the rest of his toast by dropping it on his plate and gave Bryce his absolute attention. "Would you care to elaborate?"

"There's nothing much to elaborate. I'm just saying that Paul is not being entirely honest. One, he did not argue with his wife. And two, if Roxanne was telling the truth, he was supposed to go somewhere and he never arrived. I don't suppose there were any fingerprints."

"Nothing interesting so far," Angelo answered. "The place looks like it was wiped down. One set's so smeared it's useless."

Bryce seemed to further surprise Angelo by asking: "Did you get that jacket to Reno like I asked?"

"Yeah. Late yesterday afternoon."

Bryce nodded. Through his mind ran two short, ambiguous phrases: . . . *sailing, sailing with some dude . . . short, chubby little fart*.

"I think you better find him again. Bring him in for questioning."

"Sure. You got questions you want to ask, I'll get him," he said, looking as if he had questions of his own. "You going to let me in on any of this?"

Bryce paused. "Give me till tomorrow. Find Reno. And let me have the Gautiers—just until this afternoon. I'll see them after we leave here—by then I might be able to supply you with something that makes sense," he ended cautiously.

Angelo screwed his mouth around and then nodded. "Yeah, sure, whatever you say. I'll hold Reno until you show, and pray he doesn't lift half the station while he's in there. Kid's got sticky fingers—born with Krazy Glue on them. Last time I had him in, he lifted a paperweight, two candy bars, and a pack of cigarettes off my desk."

Bryce smiled but made no comment and Angelo regarded him with a certain amount of concern.

As Bryce knew well, Angelo was a worrier. He worried excessively and, often, without reason. But Bryce also knew that Angelo derived security from this practice, for he was aware of the many pitfalls of this world, and in expressing them, felt he fulfilled an important function—like a warning sign on a highway, or a map that pinpoints specific spots of danger. It was his way of reaching out and touching people. And as it often had in the past, Bryce could see Angelo's concern heading in his direction. He waited, wondering what turn Angelo's mind would take this time.

"This Gautier woman—the one who does the paintings—you know her well?"

"Some."

Angelo paused, nodding, his face serious. "How's your girlfriend? Talked to her since you've been here? Is she doing okay?"

"Yes, I've talked to her and, yes, she's fine," Bryce answered a little impatiently. "Why do you ask?"

"Just wondering, just wondering. You always got to stay in touch—or so I understand," Angelo said, letting his eyes trail off in another direction. "You're looking pretty good nowadays. Healthy."

"I see," commented Bryce dryly. First Laura and now Angelo. Why was everyone so concerned about Katharine's welfare? For God's sake, Angelo didn't even know her. What about me? Bryce thought. *I'm* the poor idiot besotted with a young woman who can't say three normal words. Bryce's mouth took a slightly harder set.

"I'm just concerned," his friend said. "I've seen you fuck up one relationship—hate to see you fuck up another."

Bryce gave him a glance, more exasperated than angry, and Angelo held his hands in the air as if he were stopping traffic.

"None of my business—"

"Angelo," Bryce said, with a look that would have stopped most others. "Has it ever occurred to you that you're not the world's mother?"

"Has it ever occurred to you, Kevin Bryce, that you've always been one cagey son of a bitch?"

The two men glared at one another. The bill arrived and they both made a dive for it. Bryce came up with the check, waving it briefly, out of Angelo's reach.

"Stability, Angelo, enjoy it."

Angelo leaned forward and whispered: "Fuck you, Kevin Bryce. Fuck *you*."

Bryce started laughing.

CHAPTER FIFTEEN

■

Bryce drove directly into the garage beneath the Gautier apartment building and parked the Mercedes. Perhaps instructions had been left with the guard, for he sat at his desk watching a video record Bryce's ascent in the elevator without stopping it to question him.

Kim, head down, makeup markedly more discreet, answered the door and mutely led Bryce to the study. Paul sat at his desk, his back erect, a silver pencil in hand, positioned in much the same way Bryce had observed judges sit as they presided over a trial. Roxanne leaned against the pool table, her hands jammed into the pockets of a long smocklike sweater. In contrast to Kim, she was made-up much less discreetly, her delicate features heavily painted. It reminded Bryce of a line he had read the night before: *. . . with a brush between my fingers, my hand becomes steady . . .*

"I know what's happened," Bryce said quietly, and Paul looked at him with an expression masked by a jigsaw of emotions: grief, anger, suspicion, the fundamental desire to believe something good. "There are things to be done, and they need to be done quickly," Bryce continued.

Paul roused himself. "Listen, you don't have to—"

"You wanted to know about Taylor, didn't you? And I assume you want to know about your brother," Bryce told him. Gautier looked as if he were about to challenge him, but changed his mind. "I have reason to believe one may affect the other," Bryce finished.

But Paul was no longer looking at him. He was staring at Roxanne.

"Well, can you tell us, Roxanne?" Paul asked her. "Does one affect the other?"

Not one muscle on her face moved. She regarded the floor as unblinkingly as though, on top of everything else, she had suddenly gone deaf.

Paul opened his mouth to speak again, but Bryce interrupted him.

"I have some questions to ask both of you. Also, I want us to go to your studio, Roxanne."

Seemingly against their wills, they responded to the authority of Bryce's professional tone. Paul rose from his desk, his resistance manifested in an impatient rap of his knuckles on the desk in time with each step he took around it. Roxanne merely blinked and followed Paul. At the studio door she hesitated, absently patting her sweater pockets, her pants pockets.

"I'm sorry . . . my keys . . . I'll have to get them. . . ."

"Perhaps," Bryce said gently, "Paul can use his."

Paul froze. Roxanne seemed to snap out of whatever spell it was that held her.

"Could we?" Bryce persisted respectfully.

After a pause, Paul produced a key ring from the right-hand pocket of his trousers. Roxanne appeared mesmerized by this activity. Pleasure flitted across her face; so quickly that it was only because Bryce understood her character so well he was sure it had been there at all. Paul avoided her eyes as she led them into her studio.

"First of all," Bryce began, directing himself to Paul, "I need to know what it was that your brother told you."

Paul remained silent. He put his hands on his narrow hips and walked to the other end of the studio, then arched his back—as if in stretching the muscles about his spine, he was also strengthening those of his resolve. His head turned slightly, exhibiting his profile—the strong nose, too refined to be described as Roman; the beard, though trimmed, still with enough substance to convey the command and potency of an Old Testament judge; the brow, creased with both determination and question. Turning farther, Bryce noted the faintest hint of guilt in Paul's eyes.

"Are you working with the police?" Paul asked.

"Unofficially."

Paul delayed his response a few moments more. Bryce waited with a veneer of patience.

"Rob . . . Rob, you must understand, has always had his own way of doing things. It's a trait we've all inherited in one way or another. He has—had—good manners, and he was a hard worker . . . but a little impatient with the slower, more conventional methods of attaining prosperity," he concluded diplomatically. "Our parents were comfortable enough, encouraging, but never what one would term open-handed. They didn't believe it would be in our best interests. I think Rob found that attitude a bit more . . . problematic than the rest of us did.

"Rob got through Stanford, but considering the grades he got in some classes, I'd be surprised if he got them all by putting his nose to the grindstone. There were stories that got back to Mom and Dad—stories about booze, parties, fights, the usual college antics—that worried them. There were other stories that got back to me, through friends, that were more serious . . . that he was able to gain access to the university computer, find out the answers to test questions ahead of time, even change certain test scores, sometimes whole class grades. He was supposed to have helped friends who had got themselves in trouble—and himself, of course. If those stories were true, then he was very successful. He was never caught. Or if he was, he was able to talk his way out of it. He was genuinely good-natured—very affectionate—and because of that, he could always convince someone he would be better next time, always get someone on his side.

"Anyway," Paul continued, thrusting the tips of his fingers in the back pockets of his pants, "after college he got a job—"

"What kind of job?"

"A good starting position with a computer consulting firm. Things seemed to be going well. Mom and Dad were pleased."

Bryce was suddenly aware of Roxanne. She was sitting on the window seat, watching the sky rather than Paul, as if her greatest concern lay in something beyond those four walls.

"But you were less satisfied?" Bryce prompted.

"Rob was always one for shortcuts. If there's one thing I've learned in the past ten years, it's that people don't change all that much—or not as much as one would like," he amended. He shifted the position of his hands and continued. "Although Rob wasn't exactly throwing money away, his spending did seem a little more inflated than I thought his income would allow. Especially when I heard through the grapevine that he was investing heavily in various properties around town."

"Did you ever confront him with any of this?"

"My brother was over eighteen," Paul replied. "What he did with himself was his own business." His sarcasm made Roxanne lift her head.

"And did he ask for your help finally?" Bryce questioned gently.

Paul sighed. "Yes. Finally. I suppose he did."

Bryce waited, but Paul was silent.

"When did you discover your brother's interest in other men?"

Paul had tears in his eyes. "When he was in college he told me. He was having a struggle over it. He liked women too. He always enjoyed female company, but more and more he had become fascinated with other men. And he'd been doing some experimenting. I think he felt guilty. He made fun of Mom and Dad, but at the same time he was very attached to them. He was wondering whether or not to tell them. I suggested that if he felt guilty, he could see a priest or a counselor. I said that later, if he wanted to live an openly gay lifestyle with another man, I'd be there if he wanted to make it known—our parents, you see, wouldn't take it well." He paused. "It's funny, but somehow it didn't come as a surprise."

"When did he last ask for your help?"

"Soon after Taylor died, I think. Within a few weeks." Paul took a deep breath and rubbed the back of his neck. "He was almost in a panic, looking for Taylor's picture collection. He hadn't been able to find it. When I asked him why, he said he thought there might be some incriminating evidence in it."

"Precisely what sort of incriminating evidence?" Bryce asked sharply.

"He wouldn't say. I tried to push to issue, since I didn't want to become involved when I didn't know what was going on. I insisted he confide in me, but..." Paul sighed and ran his fingers through his hair, "...he managed to convince me it wasn't necessary."

"And how did he do that?" Bryce asked.

"He...he was in his apartment. We were in his bedroom. He walked to the nightstand, took a key from the drawer and dangled it in front of my face. It was the key to Roxanne's studio."

"How did he get the key?"

"Taylor and Rob evidently had...an arrangement. Taylor had

been living in an apartment Rob had bought. If you know anything about Taylor at all, you know that—except for that damned photo collection—he was careless with his possessions, left them scattered all over the place. He was worried about losing Roxanne's key, so he had an extra made and gave it to Rob to keep for him."

Roxanne stared.

"The relationship between Rob and Taylor... Were they lovers?" Bryce asked. "Or was it strictly a business arrangement?"

"It was mainly a business arrangement," Paul told him softly. "But... I don't think Rob was completely satisfied with it. They may have been occasional lovers, but the impression he gave me was that he would have liked something more concrete and couldn't quite... achieve it," Paul finished delicately.

"Did you know of this relationship before Taylor died?"

"No. They were very discreet."

"Was Rob as discreet in all his relationships?"

"Apparently. Or he was until Taylor died. He was so discreet it's difficult to know what *all* his relationships entailed," Paul observed harshly.

Roxanne shifted to the farthest corner of the window seat.

"You were supposed to look for Taylor's picture collection here, correct?"

"Correct."

"Anything else?"

"No."

"What made Rob believe that it might be in Roxanne's studio?"

"His contention was that Taylor had a special relationship with my wife. He might have entrusted the collection into her care."

"Then why not approach her directly? Why go through you?"

Paul shrugged. "I don't know. I suggested it, would have insisted on it, but... he didn't seem to think she'd be willing to cooperate."

"Did he give a reason?"

"No. But he . . . insisted. Taylor left a message on Rob's answering machine the night he died. Rob played it back for me. It was only one sentence. He said, 'It's where you can't get your fucking hands on it!' That was all," Paul said absently, as if searching in this sentence for a special significance that was eluding him. "Do you know what he did after he played that tape. He *cried*. Rob was always emotional—always. But why cry? Why then?"

What do you associate with tears? Bryce wondered. Love? Hate? Well, yes, either one. But he wanted something more explicit.

"Oh, dear God," Roxanne moaned softly, and curled her knees slowly, pressing them against her chest.

The sound served the same function as waving a red cape before a bull. In a few short strides Paul was across the room, standing above her, his fury bright and potent.

"Why was he crying, Roxanne? You're the only one surviving out of this trio—what the hell was going on?"

Roxanne hugged her knees tightly, an exquisite reflection of sorrow etched on her beautiful face. "I can't tell you," she whispered.

It was an unfortunate choice of words.

"You *can't* tell me?" he repeated, chillingly deliberate. "Well, *can* you tell me where you were last night? Is *that* information available?"

"I . . . I was out to dinner. I got home around ten or so—"

"Don't lie to me. I called last night after I found Rob. Nobody answered. Where were you when I needed you? Whatever you do, Rox, *don't lie to me now.*"

"She isn't," Bryce said, his tone as sharp as it ever got.

"I *called*. If she was home, why didn't she answer?"

"I can vouch for her. She was with me," Bryce told him.

Paul swung around; his eyes narrowed and then grew wide. Whatever confusion crossed his mind was quickly resolved, then his precarious hold on his emotions was lost.

Bryce moved quickly and caught Paul's fist before it could make contact with his face. He twisted Paul's arm around and up until Paul gasped. He would have left it at that, but Paul's frustration kept his body moving long after it was sensible to do so.

He caught the buckle of Bryce's knee with his leg and they both went down with a grunt. They rolled across the studio, their momentum fueled by Paul's angry, undirected kicks, by his push to free himself from Bryce's hold. He snapped his head back and his skull smacked Bryce's cheekbone. Feeling a sharp crack of pain, one eye going black with flashes of white like lightning, Bryce hugged Paul and rolled him until Paul felt the pressure of Bryce's full weight above him, till the squeeze of his arms cut the air to his lungs. Paul groaned, and with one supreme effort pressed his hands to the floor, straining to lift them both off the ground. Out of sheer determination he might have succeeded, but Bryce had the advantage of more experience. He drove his knee between Paul's, and utilizing the force Paul had started, jerked them both to their feet. Arms locked around Paul's chest, he made a run for the blunt corner of the heavy wooden worktable, using Paul as a shield. Paul's stomach hit the edge, sank back into his spine and it was all over.

While Paul's whole body screamed for air, Bryce, breathing heavily, let him sink gently to the floor.

Roxanne stayed at her window seat.

"Now," Bryce said, when he believed Paul could hear again, "if you've got that out of your system, maybe we can get on with things."

Paul rose shakily to his feet, stunned and weak.

"As for your wife's activities," Bryce said, once again businesslike, "I arrived here at seven-thirty and we had one cocktail. Then we left for dinner. We returned here at ten-thirty, where, in this studio, we discussed Taylor and what she knew of his more current activities. The phone did ring. We did not answer," he cited clinically. "Do you have anything to add?" he asked Roxanne without turning.

"No."

"What did you do after I left?"

"I stayed here. I fell asleep on the window seat. I woke up later—I'm not sure how much later. Then I went to bed."

"There. We have an account of Roxanne's activities—" Bryce was interrupted by a tentative knock on the studio door. With utmost caution Kim peered around its corner.

"Telephone," Kim said. "It's your father, Mr. Gautier. Wants to talk to one of you."

"Paul is unavailable," Bryce said quietly. "Roxanne, you can talk to him."

"I'm sure I won't be any comfort," she protested.

"Try," he told her.

Behind his back she opened her mouth and then closed it. She got up and walked out. Kim followed, shutting the door quietly after them. Bryce continued to regard Paul seriously, though he was pleased. This small interruption had served his purpose—Roxanne was gone.

"As I was saying, we have an account of your wife's activities. Now we need an account of yours. You were supposed to have left town for a couple of days—correct?"

Paul nodded and took two ragged drags of air.

"A business trip—family business. Investments my father and I share. I was supposed to go to Los Angeles. We boarded and sat on the runway for two hours. Then we were told the plane had engine trouble and we were herded back into the terminal, where we discovered L.A. was fogged in. It was such a mess, I rescheduled my flight and came home. Thought I'd take Rox out, make sure she ate." Paul shifted his body, supporting it by resting against the table. He kept his eyes on the floor, one arm across his stomach.

"I couldn't figure out where she'd gone. She rarely calls anyone to go out—especially since Taylor... I thought she might have gone shopping... gone out to rent some movies, or to the grocery for something. I waited for about an hour, then got worried. I drove to Union Square and checked the parking garage to see if her car was there. I drove to a movie theatre she likes..."

"Did you drive to Rob's?" Bryce asked gently.

"I tried not to." He paused. "I don't know what made me drive to the marina. Maybe it was the Christmas lights. Dad always took us on drives around town to look at the lights when we were kids. That's where we'd end up with ice cream cones. I don't know," he said, shaking his head. "I saw Rob's car and... I found him."

"Why did you lie to the police?" Bryce questioned, though he could think of only one reason for an intelligent man to do such an incredibly stupid thing.

"I don't know. I hardly knew what I was saying. All I could think was, *Where was Roxanne?*"

"So, in other words, you were buying time until you could match stories with her," Bryce said, clarifying the logic both for himself and Paul, who seemed surprised at its accuracy. "Did you suspect her of Rob's murder?"

"I didn't know what to think. I feel like such a *fucking fool*—how did you know I had a key?"

"At our first meeting you mentioned the subject of Roxanne's paintings, and you included murder. But at the gallery there are no paintings showing murder. It had me puzzled until last night, when I saw the two paintings Roxanne had here. And since she told me you hadn't visited her studio since Taylor died..." Bryce finished with a slight lift to his brow that was as effective as any shrug.

"I see," Paul said, his smile both amused and sardonic.

"I don't blame you for being concerned," Bryce said quietly. "Roxanne's paintings are very... effective."

"Oh, they're effective. Very *effective,*" Paul agreed bitterly. "Their message is clear—to me if no one else. But I don't see why—"

"Do you read magazines?" Bryce interrupted, knowing he risked another roll on the floor his body had no desire for. But also knowing that if Paul was perceptive enough to see the message in Roxanne's exhibit, he was also perceptive enough to see other things. Whether he could accept them was another matter. "*Time? Newsweek?* Of course you do," Bryce said, knowing they went hand in hand with his *Forbes* and *Wall Street Journal.* "A Nobel Prize-winning poet, a Czech name Jaroslav Seifert, was quoted in one of them a while back. He said, 'If an ordinary man is silent, it may be a tactical maneuver. If a writer is silent, he is lying.' " Bryce took a moment to study his hands. "I think that same statement could easily apply to painters, as well." Bryce opened his hands and closed them again. "You wouldn't want to be married to a liar, would you?"

Paul took a short, impatient pace to the window, where the sun went in and out of the clouds, changing the mood of the scenery like someone constantly dimming the lights then perversely setting them on bright again.

"That isn't what I want to hear. I want a reasonable solution . . . a constructive alternative."

You want what you want, Bryce thought. You want your brother alive, you want the possibility of being deceived inconceivable, you want to reach to your wife's heart in the night and find some response to your touch. Don't we all?

"You want a constructive alternative?" Bryce countered. "Give her half of what you have and throw her out on her ass."

Paul turned, startled, perhaps expecting to see a hardness in Bryce's face to accompany his ungentle words. But he saw no malice, not for him or Roxanne.

"I've always been the nice one, the sensible one, the *good* one," Paul said, almost to himself. "Pope Paul the Good, Rob used to call me. Sometimes, I would get mad. Once, when we were kids, I punched him—in the stomach.'' Unconsciously, he touched his own stomach. ''So Dad wouldn't see any marks. Rob loved it... didn't change his opinion.'' Paul's eyes slowly met Bryce's. ''Somehow it hasn't done me a lot of good. The one thing I want most... it works against me.''

For a few moments the only sound in the room was their breathing, Bryce's slow and quiet, Paul's labored.

''It takes a certain courage to go after what we really want,'' Bryce said softly, and thought that once again Katharine was right: brave and foolhardy did go hand in hand.

''When you say Rob insisted that Roxanne wouldn't be cooperative, did he give any specifics? You're not a stupid man, Paul. In many ways you've been very clear in your understanding of your wife. I assume you're that way about your brother also. Did he give any reasons—or did he just play with Roxanne's relationship to Taylor?''

''He... he played on me. Taylor's homosexuality didn't really seem something you could take for granted—there was this masculinity about him too. And Roxanne was so attached to him, you see—more than I think she realized. Rob managed to convey that Taylor's guarded relations with him might indicate less guarded relations with her. But even then,'' Paul corrected himself, ''Rob was so vague, there could have been any number of possibilities.''

Under the correct circumstances, Bryce reasoned, even an unimaginative man can become very imaginative.

''I was afraid there had been some bizarre three-ring circus going on while I was being tolerant to the point of foolishness.''

Bryce nodded. ''I don't imagine you were pushy about details, were you?''

Paul looked at Bryce and then away again.

''No,'' he said. ''But I've had months to think it over. I have to admit it's preyed on my mind. How was Rox involved? Those pictures . . . those pictures she painted . . . and Taylor modeling for them—"

Bryce glanced at Paul sharply, then turned his attention to his own hands.

Paul said, "Could she, accidentally or otherwise, become party to—what? Blackmail, maybe? Or just adultery? I suppose that's why I got in contact with you. Katharine spoke highly of you. If I really was an idiot, then I wanted to know it for a fact."

Bryce resisted the temptation to appear too sympathetic. "The adultery doesn't interest me," he said. "That is your business, not mine. Do you love her? Does life seem more interesting, fuller, because in the evening you can have dinner and talk to her—at night you can go to bed with her?"

Paul didn't answer.

"If so, then perhaps it's better to enjoy that and not ask too much—"

"Is it too much to want your wife to be honest and faithful?" Paul shot at him angrily. *"She made a promise!"*

"Yes, well, true," Bryce agreed dryly. "But if you helped compromise her honesty once out of ignorance, don't do it again out of sheer stubbornness. You can't get mad at her for not being what you want her to be. And if you can't take what she is, if it's not worth it to you. . . ." Bryce shrugged. "There's an old proverb about getting out of the kitchen if you can't take the heat."

Paul whispered something Bryce couldn't quite catch.

"When you said Rob was discreet—or was until Taylor died—did you mean that since that time he had been less discreet?"

"A little more careless, a lot more promiscuous, almost flamboyant about it with me. He may have been seeing a woman too."

"What makes you think that?"

"Once a week or so he'd say something like, 'I'm going to

see an angel tonight.' Sometimes it was his 'Angel without mercy.' I just assumed it was a woman because he always called her Angel."

Bryce repressed a smile. When Roxanne walked in a few seconds later, even she noted a difference in him, a clearer sense of direction, the kind of pleasure that comes when the pieces, however awful, start falling into place.

"I was just about to call for you. I need to see what Taylor left here that last afternoon. You have it all, don't you? In that drawer in the cabinet, correct?"

Roxanne nodded dumbly, then went to the cabinet. As she had before, she opened a cassette case and two keys fell out. She took one and unlocked the drawer while Paul watched from the far end of the room. Roxanne emptied the drawer onto the table.

There was the change Taylor had once so carefully stacked; stacked even now, since in an odd gesture, Roxanne had Scotch-taped them together. Bryce methodically set the piles side by side. There were a lot of quarters. Video games, he thought. Dimes. Pennies. One nickel. Sunglass case, a pair of Carrera sunglasses inside. A cheap key ring with five keys, one very small, as to a lock box. Ticket stubs, torn in half. One to the Star Theatre, one to a theater whose first three letters were BAL, another whose last three were GUE. Inside the leather wallet was a hundred dollar bill, three twenties, two fives, six ones. There were receipts. Plain white ones for two dollars, whose blue ink read MEMBERS FREE, JOIN TODAY. One to a graphic arts supply store for $27.67. An identification card—no driver's license. A Macy's credit card in the name of R. A. Gautier. Pictures. Pretty girls. Reno. Two of Roxanne. A variety of business cards. Bingo chips from Safeway.

Bryce pulled a notebook from his sweater pocket. He made a list of what he found and signed the bottom.

"A little unorthodox," he said, handing it to Roxanne, "but it should work. Did he leave anything else?"

"Not the last time—except for a cap. But he did have some record albums, if you want those."

"Please," he said, and she turned to take them from the collection on the shelf.

Bryce returned her car keys. "I'll call a cab from downstairs," he said, and she nodded impassively.

Bryce glanced from husband to wife. He let the air out of his lungs. His need for them temporarily over, he left them to their own devices.

Chapter Sixteen

■

The excuse Bryce used was a flimsy one. Under the half-true, half-invented pretext of needing to see the owner, he strolled into the gallery on Sutter. He was not disappointed to discover there would be a delay. On the contrary, it suited him just fine.

He conducted a tour for himself; moving from canvas to canvas, past an occasional blank space where a painting had been sold. Views from a window. Bryce peered from pane to pane, trying to judge the whole scenario from what was visible through each small, selective framework.

Portrayals. As honest as one knows how to make them; the job many an artist attempts to undertake. They challenge us to evaluate ourselves. In doing so, they stir our emotions, make us aware of our own lack of health. Certainly Roxanne had done this. As if, like a good doctor, she had pointed it out on a chart to him. And maybe, like a good doctor, she did not allow herself to be too touched by the misery around her. But also, like a good doctor, she ran into the danger of becoming callous, even of falling victim to all the diseases she ministered to.

And Paul. Roxanne was Paul's walk on the wild side. But there was a risk involved. His walk could take him further than his conservative nature would allow. *Take me, but don't take me too far!*

Hypocrisy. Didn't we all have it in some form? Certainly Bryce had his hypocrisies, his selfishness.

"Why did you go into police work?" Katharine had asked him once.

"I had to earn a living," he'd replied. "I couldn't afford to go to college for five or six years—I had my son to support. And I was a little rebellious. The choice seemed to be the police or the army. I chose the police because I didn't want to live in the barracks with a bunch of men. I like my privacy. I also like women. I like living with a woman—they're good companions."

"Then why hadn't you had one since your wife left?" she'd asked.

The answer was, of course, because he liked his writing more. More than his wife, anyway. And more than any other woman he had met until Katharine.

On the other hand, he could tell himself he loved Katharine more than he had anyone else. Or that he had learned how to conduct a relationship with more maturity. But the truth of the matter was, he might not ever really know. He was not blind to his own hypocrisy. He could afford to be generous with himself now. He was financially secure, he could do his writing at whatever pace suited him, and on the whole, it was fairly well-received. The time he took to give to someone else was rarely time away from his work. There was little sacrifice involved. Katharine, needing privacy herself, rarely intruded on his own.

There was no room for him to be condescending to either Roxanne or Paul. Or possibly even to Rob.

"Mr. Bryce? Can I do something for you?" The man was

short, well-dressed, and the tiniest bit prissy. He approached Bryce with the seasoned sales representative's mixture of confidence and concern. Bryce smiled, fudged a little on his association with the SFPD, and then asked about Taylor.

"I know it was in September, but could you give me an idea what time he was here?"

The man was quick and precise. Taylor, evidently, was well etched in his memory. After all, he'd been tending his likeness for months. The gallery owner came in at eleven every morning. Taylor was there at 11:05.

And what, Bryce was left to wonder, did he do between eleven and four-thirty?

"You're getting too old for this kind of shit," Angelo muttered, and handed Bryce his version of an ice pack—ice cubes in a plastic sandwich bag. The bag had been a leftover from Angelo's lunch, and still had crumbs of white bread and small moist spots of peanut butter and strawberry jam smeared against the inside. Bryce winced as he touched the pack to his swollen cheek. "You're approaching the time of life when these things could do you some damage, you know," Angelo said.

"Thanks," Bryce commented dryly.

"No wonder that gallery guy didn't ask for any identification. Probably took one look at that shiner and decided to take pity on you."

Bryce took the pack from his face, giving it a sour look before gingerly pressing it back. "No Reno?" he asked.

"Not a sign. But it's still early." Angelo didn't sound hopeful. He lit a cigarette and took a deep drag, regarding Bryce pensively. "You gonna explain the face or is that another thing you're not going to tell me? I am the police. Somebody's got to tell me something sometime."

"That's a feeble plea if I ever heard one."

"Maybe. But it's the only one I got, so I use it." Angelo

paused. "Just a little enlightenment, Kevin. That's all I'm asking."

Bryce sat in a chair opposite Angelo's desk and braced one foot on the corner of its rim. Slowly, from time to time taking the pack from his face, he explained how he became involved: the letter, Katharine encouraging him to go, his first meeting with Paul Gautier and the man's vagueness in regard to Roxanne.

"Typical," Angelo said.

Bryce recounted his dinner with Roxanne and Paul; then his dinner alone with Roxanne, though there were certain aspects of it he left out. He did, however, tell Angelo about Roxanne's journal.

"You read this thing?" Angelo asked.

"Last night."

Angelo whistled through his teeth. "You've been a busy little boy. Is any of the stuff in there useful?"

"All of it," Bryce answered absently. He touched the pack to his cheek and looked up to find Angelo sitting on his desk, watching him almost eagerly. "If you're asking me if any of it can be submitted in court as solid evidence, the answer is, probably not."

"Wouldn't expect that. Not at all. Just naturally figure that would be asking too much," Angelo said, without disappointment. He stubbed out a freshly lit cigarette. "So, for the time being, why don't you just tell me what you think I ought to know."

Bryce did. He carefully detailed the contents of Roxanne's private journal. Then, slowly emptying his pockets of the items Taylor had left in the studio onto Angelo's desk, he recounted his morning's visit with the Gautiers.

Angelo pursed his lips and said: "I told you family matters get messy." He watched Bryce touch the pack to his cheek and asserted: "That Gautier must have a hard head in more ways than one."

"He's frustrated," Bryce said simply.

"If he's frustrated, let him beat his wife rather than you. Some people need to be knocked around. It's good for their character."

Bryce smiled and instantly regretted it. He pressed the ice pack tighter to his cheek.

"So let me see if I understand the situation," Angelo said, pointing at him. Bryce reflected that Angelo was probably one of those people who, deprived of the use of their hands, would be unable to utter a word. "We have this artist, Roxanne, right? Ten years ago she waltzes into San Francisco and her biggest worry in life is how to get enough time to do the painting she wants to do. Fine. Great. We all have our ambitions, right? She's got a point—families are distracting, and they ain't always so rewarding either. Hers sure didn't sound like any prize. On the other hand it's programmed into us to need *somebody*. People are a communal species. But this gal is doing pretty good on her own.

"Then your girlfriend—what's her name? Katharine?—enters the picture. An independent, financially secure young woman who Gautier is kinda interested in. But she takes one look at Gautier and the in-laws and reads the writing on the wall. Smart gal, your Katharine. So on her introduction, enter Gautier into the story. Your typical patriarch. Responsible. Kind. Maybe even wise on occasion. Knows for man to be alone is not good, and isn't afraid to admit it. However, like any leader worth his salt, he is strong-willed. Like any young idiot, he doesn't think he will fail. He would have made a great Knight of the Round Table. In World War One he would have died in the trenches. Anyway," said Angelo, gaining momentum, "he meets Roxanne—to people who can't draw or write a song or make a coherent sentence, these sorts of talents seem almost mystical. They take pride in knowing someone who has them. On top of it, the woman is charming, good-looking. In the great tradition of opposites attracting opposites, he falls for her. As I said before, it is not good for man to be alone, and Gautier decides it ain't so hot for Roxanne either. Roxanne, however, is content to be a selfish flake. And Gautier, who is human, is not above a certain selfishness and stupidity himself. He also has your basic peasant cunning. He uses the same technique a lot of strong countries use to get power over weaker countries. He makes himself indispensible, then pulls the rug out. Good strategy. It's a mistake to put Gautier in the saint category. Here's a man who knows where to punch so the marks don't show—just like he did to his brother. Gautier would have made a good criminal if he'd only had the disposition for it.

"But he doesn't have the disposition, unfortunately. He's not content to be a little unscrupulous, he also wants to be right. He wants 'romance.' I wonder if it's the movies that brought that into our culture," Angelo mused. He lit another cigarette. "But after a while he begins to realize he's got a wife on his hands who's missing a few pieces. The wife, no stranger to her own faults, has been uncomfortable, even miserable, but her number one goal—to paint—has been achieved. How am I doing so far?"

"You should have been a psychologist, Angelo," Bryce said with amusement.

"I was a probation officer once. That's close enough," Angelo answered seriously. He dropped his cigarette in a cluttered ashtray and leaned forward. "Okay. So a few years later enter Taylor. Now we have Roxanne and Taylor, two of a kind, but Roxanne is the only one that knows it. Taylor, who sees everything through the haze of the latest movie, only knows he's finally with someone he feels comfortable with. She doesn't give, she doesn't take, and she appears to be everything he ever wanted. They have a nice if somewhat unrealistic relationship. And he keeps coming back for more. Maybe he falls in love with her. You say they never went to bed together?" Angelo asked, as if he found this more than he could gracefully accept.

"No, never," Bryce said.

Angelo frowned. "Surprises me," he said.

"When I talked to Reno, he told me Taylor had been on the streets too long, that he wasn't doing so well with women anymore. That some of Taylor's girlfriends even remarked on it."

Angelo brightened. "Now that makes sense. The fear of failure. And not just of your usual screw-up—if you'll pardon the expression—but a grand fuck-up. Suppose he's no good with the one person he wants to be good with?" Angelo did not pursue the possibilities aloud. "Do you think it would have made any difference?"

"No," Bryce answered slowly, "probably not. In this case."

"Too bad. If they had, I wonder if it would have short-circuited this whole disaster."

Bryce did not attempt to confirm or deny. Angelo absently fingered his pockets for cigarettes.

"Son of a bitch," he said, finding them. Between lighting, he continued: "In the meantime brother Rob has snuck on to the scene. We have Taylor goggle-eyed over this woman he's scared to death to touch but doesn't want to lose. So what does he do? He wants to be a part of the family. Even, maybe, become somewhat legitimate. So he hooks up with brother Rob.

"Now Rob has problems of his own. People always want what they cannot have. Rob wants to be rich—fast—and Rob wants more of Taylor. Rob is also a family man. He wants to bring his partner home to Mama and Papa. But Mama and Papa would be less than thrilled. And no doubt the last thing Taylor wants is to be exposed to his Madonna as Rob's faggot friend. I wish to *hell* I knew what Rob and Taylor were up to."

Bryce dropped his melted bag of ice into the trash.

"Anyway," Angelo continued, "a situation like this is bound to cause tension. And have you noticed how certain problems seem to run in the family? We've got Paul and Roxanne. And now Rob and Taylor. Criminey, for all we know, they may have started in pretty much the same way. Rob may have been attracted to Taylor because he was so damned good-looking—

remember what I told you about the Marilyn Monroe syndrome? Or maybe it was Taylor's imagination. They become friends—Rob was a nice guy, no doubt. Very helpful, considerate, encouraging. Does he really *need* Taylor's help for anything? Probably not. But he wants to keep him close. He gives him something to do, sets him up with a place to live.

"Now, Rob's a white-collar boy. Suppose—let's just suppose—whatever he sets Taylor up with is a white-collar crime. Hell, after what Taylor's seen in this world, it probably won't even seem like a crime to him. A clean cheat, maybe; a crime, no. In doing so, Taylor develops a new skill, something he could eventually use legitimately. Something like—I don't know—*photography.* Taylor, with his love of pictures, that would be logical.

"And what might also be possible," Angelo said, reaching new levels of enthusiasm, "is that Rob doesn't even tell him it's a crime. Taylor would be so ignorant of Rob's world, he might not realize what he's doing. This is part of my work, Rob says, help me, learn this and you'll be doing you and me both a favor. Great arrangement.

"But things get sticky when Rob wants a little more personal commitment. Taylor isn't so good at that. When Rob applies too much pressure, Taylor hits the streets for one of his occasional binges. Whether Rob knew all along about Taylor's attachment for Roxanne is another interesting question we'll never know the answer to. My educated guess is that he did but didn't know how strong it was, and like his brother, thought through goodwill and persistence he could change him. Like his brother, he was wrong.

"So time goes by and Rob can't see himself making much progress into Taylor's affection. Maybe one day—who knows? —Taylor's talking about Roxanne, singing her praises. Or maybe he's gonna spend the evening with her when Rob wants him, Rob gets extra pissed. Maybe he comes unglued—it happens. Niceness hasn't busted this infatuation to hell, so let's try another method.

Informs Taylor that his little Roxanne has painted some fine and dandy pictures of him and he should go take a look. Maybe he thought Taylor would come running to him for comfort. Or maybe he was so mad he didn't care.'' Angelo paused, thoughtfully sucking on his cigarette. ''Paul seems to be wiser.''

Bryce didn't say anything.

''Anyway,'' Angelo concluded, ''it backfired.''

Even this sublime example of understatement failed to elicit a response from Bryce.

''So,'' Angelo said, moving onward, ''we have Rob feeling miserable and guilty, Roxanne feeling like a piece of meat, and Paul probably even feeling sorry for the little fucker. But Paul's real concern is his wife. She don't look so good, which probably irritates the hell out of Rob, who probably blames Roxanne more than he does himself since that seems to be the way of the world—to pass the buck whenever possible. And she, of course, is by no means innocent.

''And we are not without a certain sibling rivalry here,'' Angelo surmised knowledgeably. ''What did Rob call his brother—the pope? Everybody believes in Paul's basic niceness—even his wife, and that's saying something. But when you're a royal fuck-up and your brother is Mister Wonderful, well, it's a situation a lot of people would find irritating. Then when his wife is the wet dream of the one you want yourself—my God,'' Angelo said, waving his arms, slicing through smoke. ''And throw in the guilt on top of that—you have what we have. Little brother muddying the waters between the pope and the whore.''

Angelo got up and searched his desk drawers for a bottle of bourbon. He didn't find one. ''Son of a bitch,'' he said, giving up. His eye was caught by the neat and precise line up of Taylor's personal effects. ''Then, too, if Roxanne finds out how Taylor found out about that exhibit, Rob wouldn't be real excited. Jesus.''

Bryce stirred in his chair.

"What did you think of the exhibit, Angelo, when you saw it?"

Angelo sighed, energetically rubbing the back of his neck. "It hurt. If that shit is about her, I feel sorry for her. I feel sorry for Taylor. And for Paul. Even Rob, the little shithead. I feel sorry for everyone," he declared without dramatics. "I'm a sympathetic kind of guy."

Bryce got up to pace to the window. Through the dirt on its surface he could see the variegated skyline of San Francisco and the cars passing swiftly on the freeway overpass a few yards beyond him.

"I don't especially feel any sympathy for Rob," Bryce said softly. "I do for Paul. Even for Roxanne. I feel for Taylor." He paused. "But do you know who, right at the moment, I feel for the most?—Reno."

Angelo distracted himself by playing with the Scotch-taped stacks of Taylor's coins. He repeated a short, foul sexual epitaph and looked discouraged.

"So what do we have here?" Angelo demanded. "Taylor tells Roxanne he's giving her everything he has, so where's his picture collection?" he asked irritably.

Bryce moved slowly from the window to the desk. "Do you have a newspaper? And a city map?"

"Yeah. Sure. Anything you want," Angelo said, and took a map from the desk drawer. He wandered out of his office into the hall and came back a few minutes later, newspaper in hand. Bryce opened it to the theatre section.

"Star . . . Four-Star . . . BAL . . . Balboa . . . GUE . . . Vogue. Look, Angelo," Bryce said, "look at the addresses of these theatres. Clement and Twenty-third . . . Thirty-eighth and Balboa . . . Sacramento and Presidio . . . And the address of the graphics shop—the seven thousand block of California—"

"I see your point. All in the same area. All a long way from downtown. Living out there, Taylor wasn't likely to run into any of his friends from the Tenderloin."

Bryce picked up a white receipt and examined it. MEMBERS FREE, JOIN TODAY.

"A gym?" Angelo suggested.

Bryce shook his head. The muscles around his jaw were tense. He studied the map of the city.

"A museum."

"A *museum*?"

"Katharine and I visited several when we were in town last, and there's one in that area. Lincoln Park. The Palace of the Legion of Honor," he said, putting his finger to the spot.

"Could be the De Young—it's not that far away."

"No," Bryce insisted. "My guess is Lincoln Park. It's more private than Golden Gate Park."

Angelo shrugged. "So what does that tell us? A little culture finally rubs off on Taylor and he visits a museum once."

"Not once. There are two other receipts in his wallet. It's the kind of thing you do. Someone hands you change and a receipt, and you put the whole wad in your wallet. Like the bingo cards from the supermarket."

Angelo rubbed his eyes wearily. "So what?"

"So, we know the museum was a place he liked to go, a place he was used to going. And he had five unaccounted-for hours the last day of his life."

"You think he went to the museum to contemplate suicide. You don't need a museum to do that. . . ."

Taking the receipt with the latest date between two fingers, Bryce handed it to Angelo. "Look it up."

Angelo did while Bryce sat behind the desk absently rearranging the slim clues before him.

"So you're right," Angelo said, unsurprised. "The dates match."

"And so are you," Bryce said. "Taylor didn't need to go to a museum to contemplate suicide—but he *did* go."

"And you think there's a reason for it?"

"Taylor spends the afternoon at the museum, then visits

Roxanne and more or less calmly tells her he's bequeathing to her everything he owns. This was as much a plot of revenge as it was of desperation.'' Bryce stopped to study the receipt from the graphics store. ''Jesus,'' he said, and started laughing.

''What's this, humor? Or hysteria?''

''It's simple,'' Bryce said. ''Taylor *did* have an imagination. Especially if he imagined Roxanne would take the time to figure this out,'' he commented dryly. ''It's obscure, but here it is. He has them where they're safe and guarded all the time.''

''Kevin,'' Angelo said, ''I hate to disillusion you, but if you think Taylor's pictures are locked up in the Palace of the Legion of Honor, I got news for you. How the hell could he get it in? They don't just let you sashay in there with packages under your arm, you know. They even look at ladies' handbags suspiciously. You've got to remember, Taylor's collection is massive.''

''A museum is always encouraging and helpful to students. It's their function. Students regularly come in with books and sketchpads. They can sit undisturbed for hours.'' Bryce handed the graphics receipt to Angelo and then gave his attention to Taylor's wallet. ''Look at it, Angelo. A book on fifteenth-century art. Two large sketchbooks. One pencil. Paste.''

''Once again, Kevin, I hate to be a party pooper, but I'm telling you, Taylor had a *lot* of pictures.''

''Possibly,'' Bryce said, ''but my guess is that not all of the pictures are in the museum.''

''Then where are they?''

Bryce continued to methodically inspect the wallet's plastic card file. ''At Rob's, I should imagine. Or rather, the apartment Rob allowed Taylor to live in. You see, there would be no point in keeping the whole collection. The collection was Taylor's imaginary lives, his imaginary family, his fantasy, his work of art, if you will. Something he accumulated as a brochure on his importance. Once that was shattered, he had no more use for them. It would be logical for him to take only what was useful, and I expect that pared down his collection a good deal.''

"So what are we supposed to do? Tear up the place looking for a few photographs on a hunch? I tell you, Kevin, like a lead balloon this is going to go over with the powers that be."

Bryce drew a picture clipped out of a book on art from behind two pictures of Roxanne. He studied it as Angelo peered curiously over his shoulder. Working his face into a frown, Angelo said softly: "Well, I guess that takes care of that."

Chapter Seventeen

■

"Well, son of a bitch."

The lid was heavy and stiff, and the security guard, his crisp blue uniform jacket straining against his belly, grunted quietly as he held it in position. Oblivious to the man, the only visible part of Angelo was his compact rear and legs, dangling from the rim of the fifteenth-century walnut chest carved with scenes of the passion of Christ.

"Look at this," he called. "Looks like we hit the jackpot. Congratulations, Kevin."

Bryce stood apart from the small crowd of police and museum officials, with an elderly woman who gave tours. Her wrinkled face managed to convey both worry and excitement, and she clasped the lapels of her sweater together with one bony hand like it was a rosary from which she derived strength.

She whispered: "I remember when he used to come in. He was such a nice boy. Liked to sit in front of the portraits especially. The impressionists too. But the portraits in particular—"

"Kevin, take a look. I'm not sure what all this is, but one of our resident experts probably will. The shit is gonna hit the fan,'' Angelo said with some satisfaction. ''I think I like this. Unlike some others, this looks like the kind of crime that can be prosecuted.''

Bryce took the sketchbook, opening it without haste. Small, silver transistor junctions, connected with bits of copper wire, a unit perhaps an inch and a half in length, were photographed clearly, closely, from various angles. There were photos of those small electrical boards, lying one on the other like a club sandwich, each labeled with a neatly written series of letters and numbers. At regular intervals through these photos were others of Robin Gautier in casual clothes. Sailing clothes. He was with various other casually dressed men, men who were for the most part Asian.

''Background looks like Angel Island,'' Angelo remarked.

The camera angles were often odd. In a very small percentage, a bit of foliage or a slim stem of teak paneling was caught by the camera. The photos had been taken covertly. The position of the men also suggested a certain furtiveness, an exchange of one envelope for another. A pocket pasted on the last page was filled with negatives.

''This is great stuff,'' Angelo asserted. ''The street instinct—you just can't lose it and you can't underestimate it. Taylor was really covering his ass. But I would have preferred to find this before Gautier was cut up. It doesn't lead us any closer to our killer.''

On this disappointing observation, Angelo took back the sketchbook and joined a close circle of grim-faced museum officials to tidy the details of procedure.

Bryce paced slowly down the hall. The Palace of the Legion of Honor is a classical structure, a replica of the Palais de Salon in Paris, possessing all the grandeur of a Cecil B. De Mille movie prop. Set high on a hill, there is a golf course to one side, forest and cliff and ocean on the other. To enter the building Bryce had passed through a garden square lined with columns.

At the end of the square, inscribed above the rotunda entrance, he had read the words HONNEUR ET PATRIE, had seen stone laurel leaves impressed upon the wall. Now he found himself back in the rotunda, the nucleus. On his right were the halls of nineteenth-century France. And to his left—not for the first time—Taylor came alive for him. Bryce saw his athletic figure framed against the arch of the Louis XV hall, heard his steps on the polished parquet floor as they echoed off its high ceiling. Followed his slow progress to the end, where he turned, passing into the Medieval gallery with its low, false ceiling, its dark walls, its marble floor so old that whatever polish it had in the beginning had completely worn through. Taylor checks behind occasionally as he makes his way past the gallery's alcoves and their displays, mostly religious—tapestry apostles, limestone holy trinities, alabaster Madonnas and child. He glances from side to side to make sure he is alone, observed only by those silent representations of history.

He is startled by the click of a heel. He eases onto an oak bench in front of his designated safe-deposit box—sketchbook open, pencil in hand—and listens, counting each step the visitor takes, breathing easier as the sound fades. A guard makes his round through the hall. Taylor smiles and nods to him. The guard smiles back, disinterested. Taylor waits, then quietly moves to the center aisle. Seeing no one, he jumps back into the alcove. Taking a sketchbook, he puts first one long leg and then the other over the rail. Quietly he shoulders the lid of the chest open; his face cringes as he hopes each creak and groan is not as loud as it seems to him.

He lets it down silently, takes a second to polish the rim with his sleeve, wipe his hands on his pants. He is over the rail, gathering his book—his other sketchpad—tucking them close under his arm. He sticks the pencil behind his ear and moves down the hall with the graceful stroll of the accomplished and the physically fit. He whistles, just a bar or two, to account for any odd sounds someone might be coming to investigate. At the hallway entrance he meets an incoming guard and smiles as the man cautions him about the noise. But mostly he whistles because it seems the appropriate thing to do.

Like in a movie.

"Kevin."

Angelo was approaching, bringing Bryce to the present.

"If you're done with the free tour, can I have your attention? I've sent the photos to the station to someone who can confirm what we can already guess," Angelo told him. "I also had a thought while I was on the phone talking to my secretary. I have a lot of thoughts while talking to my secretary—most of them violent, but this one was useful, and I was able to confirm it. Robin Gautier had no keys on him, and there were none on the boat. He had to have keys. He had a car, he needed one for the gate, and I doubt the Gautiers leave their boat unlocked."

"Have you had anyone check to see what property Robin Gautier owned?"

"It was on my list of things to do."

"On second thought, you might not have to—Roxanne might have gone to the apartment Rob let Taylor live in. Remember she helped him move from an apartment on California Street to one in North Beach? She just didn't know the California address was owned by Robin."

"I'll call her. You think somebody needed the key to Taylor's old apartment?"

"Possibly."

"You don't think Rob would have gotten rid of Taylor's things and moved a new tenant in?"

Bryce frowned. "Not until he found the photographs. I don't think he would have risked getting rid of anything."

Angelo shrugged. "Makes sense. But we got a problem. If someone did go to Taylor's old digs—got in with the key so the neighbors wouldn't get nervous and holler for the police—how are we gonna know what's missing?"

Bryce smiled faintly. "We probably won't."

Angelo looked as if he would have liked to indulge in a truly perverse profanity, but catching sight of the elderly tour leader hovering nearby, checked himself.

"Let's get out of here. It's getting close to my dinnertime," he said in disgust. Together they started for the car, moving quickly through the museum, out the garden square, to the bottom of the entry stairs, to the car.

"Reno told me he didn't have much to do with the Angel."

"Uh-oh. Fib number one," Angelo said. "Reno wasn't as familiar with him as Taylor, but you can't exactly call them strangers. More since Taylor died, though. Not much at all before. But when we started putting the word out for Reno, the Angel was the first person we went to."

"And he was on the streets?"

"Yeah, cool as a cucumber," Angelo said. "We talked to Reno's mom too. But all she can talk about is her damned cats." He stopped to watch a stray dog canter across the parking lot, wild-eyed, tongue lolling. "I like dogs. Loyal, you know? But they shit all over the place."

Bryce's only comment was a smile, and Angelo gave him a sideways glance before he leaned across the car's roof, folding his hands.

"That girlfriend of yours is a gutsy little gal to send you over here by yourself. Knowing you as I do, I wouldn't let you out of my sight. Maybe she thinks what you need is a long leash."

"Angelo," Bryce said wearily.

"On the other hand, there's always the guilt angle."

It was Bryce's turn to look sideways.

"After all, she introduced those two. Introduced them with the specific intention of dumping Paul Gautier on Roxanne. But she probably didn't expect them to get married, and probably didn't think it was any wiser for Roxanne than it would have been for her. Maybe she was racked with guilt and sent you to clean up."

"Katharine experiences guilt in only its mildest forms," Bryce said dryly, then sighed.

"Tell me, I'm curious," Angelo said. "Do you love her?"

Bryce considered Angelo carefully for a few short moments before he imitated Angelo's position, folding his hands on the roof of the car and leaning forward.

"She spent the night once, and in the morning I found I didn't want her to go. The feeling," he said with splendid understatement, "has grown somewhat stronger with the passing of time."

"Oh. That's romantic as hell . . . *literally,*" Angelo retaliated.

"Did you love your wife, Angelo?"

"Yeah. Sure. I just didn't want to sleep with her, that's all. Fortunately, till the day she died, sex was never high on her list of priorities."

Distracted, Bryce said, "Did you hear that?"

"Hear what?"

Bryce didn't linger to explain. There was an observation point, part of a George Segal sculpture, located at the edge of the lot. Bryce crossed to it briskly and scrutinized the strip of forest that separated the service road below him and the cliffs that dropped to the Pacific Ocean. Loose leaves chased each other down the pavement. A cat, belly slunk low to the ground, disappeared into the brush. Directly below was the display of the Segal sculpture, *The Holocaust*. He could see the man of white plaster standing at the barbed-wire fence, saw several bunches of roses, now wilted, tributes left by museum visitors. At first glance at the pile of white plaster bodies behind the fence, the slash of color Bryce spied, seemed merely a splatter of red flowers. In the dusk, that's how well the white pants and white jacket blended into the sculpture. It took him a second to realize what it actually was.

"Angelo," Bryce called. "You better call an ambulance. I've found Reno."

"He's still alive."

"Yeah, well, that looks like a temporary condition," Angelo

whispered. "Look, there's no clotting—this couldn't have happened too long ago. Damn his *mother*." And in answer to Bryce's puzzled expression, Angelo explained: "This patch of trees runs from the bottom of the hill here at Seacliff all the way to that restaurant where we had breakfast this morning. And all through this patch is a network of shanties and lean-tos put up mostly by Reno's mother. She used to be a flower child in the Haight—but that was long before my time. Now she's a kind of bag lady who takes care of all the cats and kittens people are in the habit of abandoning here. Reno must have been hiding out in one of her shacks."

Angelo cradled Reno's head in his lap, and the boy coughed up spittle flecked with blood. "What the . . . you guys? The Angel took one . . . look at all the cop cars and . . . figured I was . . . jerking him around."

"Save it, kid. Tell us in the hospital," Angelo said.

Reno's shoulders jerked awkwardly. "Ain't gonna make it that far."

"Sure you will," Angelo said without emotion, "you're having Christmas dinner at my house."

"Fucking faggot," Reno said, with what could have been a gasp or a laugh.

"The pot calls the kettle black," Angelo responded. Reno began to cough.

At the end of his fit he was left staring at Bryce, who, kneeling beside him, touched the cuff of his sleeve and asked: "Are you the one who took the keys from Rob Gautier?"

"Pretty smart for an old man . . . eh, Angelo? Yeah, I took 'em . . . Got my pictures." His thin chest heaved. "Got the address . . . Got my pictures. You come nosing around, old man, you give me exactly what I need."

Angelo tried to hush him.

"Hey, gonna die telling a story . . . just like Taylor."

Bryce took the wool scarf from around his own neck and

tucked it firmly around Reno's blood-soaked middle. He made no attempt to stem the flow of Reno's confession.

"Was it you or the Angel who killed Rob?" he asked.

"Is that fucking wackadoo dead? . . . Well, I guess I helped. After Taylor died, I started doing more work with the Angel . . . thought if I could get in with him . . . I might learn something." Reno tried to raise himself, failing to do more than curl close into Angelo's lap. "But the Angel don't say much except that Taylor had pictures everyone wanted. You and the Angel'd get along good, old man. Don't say nothing unnecessary," Reno said tiredly, and closed his eyes. "Can't do that myself. I gotta talk."

For a minute Bryce was afraid Reno had talked his last. And Bryce, above all, wanted to know his side of the story, see the picture through his eyes, He held his breath until Reno opened his eyes and went on.

"Anyway, there's something I don't think I told you, old man . . . no offense . . . just didn't want you fucking up anything. . . . But the short chubby fart I met . . . was Rob . . . and I met the fucker more than once. The Angel set me up with him later, old man. Pure coincidence. But I tell you"—he reached up and bunched the front of Bryce's sweater in his fist—"first time I was with the bastard . . . I knew. Knew there was something . . . When the Angel brings me in, the dude acts like he don't know me. So I get the chance to make up for when I wasn't thinking so quick. I do my best to get regular with this guy . . . tight . . . like the Angel. The Angel's got a key to this guy's boat . . . find out this dude's like me. Gets a little weed in him, the dude gets kinda gabby." Reno took a brief rest. "I get bits and pieces. Figure he's the one been keepin' Taylor. More and more I get this guy to trust me . . . tell me things . . . I just wanted to know . . . wanted to know what Taylor'd been doing. Just a nosy son of a bitch, I guess . . . Sometimes knowing where he'd been I could . . . like . . . *see* him, y'know? I mean, you have to enjoy what you can.

"Anyway, talking to you, old man, made me sort of homesick.

Didn't know what to do... it was the Angel's night with Rob. Just started wandering around. Decided to go see those paintings... never seen them... thought... maybe I'd take a look.... I hung around outside the gallery for a while... Fancy place. Kinda scared to go in, y'know. Thought they might chase me out... But I did go in... And, Jesus, old man, they looked so *real*... Made me kind of sick... He... he was like that, y'know. Just like those paintings... I didn't know a painting could do that, make someone so naked.... Taylor didn't like what he was, and there it was so clear... God, no wonder he jumped off that bridge. I would've taken a dive myself.... And I thought, what kind of person would paint this, man? He'd have to be in worse shape than Taylor.... Kept looking at those paintings, old man, trying to piece it together... Weird, the way Taylor seemed to be staring in a mirror... bugged me... couldn't help it—I touched that painting... Don't know what I was trying to do—tap him on the shoulder so he'd turn around?... I looked in the corner, and the thing was signed R. Gautier, old man... couldn't believe it... that fat, brainless fart did *this*... Wondered what the fuck was going on... Some guy yelled at me. I got out of there... went to the harbor, old man. Waited in the parking lot. Wanted to take another look at this sucker... Decided I'd better play it cool... be a little smart... play with this guy's head.... Rob's surprised to see me, but he goes along with it... Be sincere. Gotta be sincere with these people..."

Bryce felt Reno's hold on his sweater grow slack. *Hurry, Reno, tell me the story quick.*

Reno grimaced, shifted his back, never taking his eyes from Bryce's face.

"I tell you, old man," he said in a voice just stronger than a whisper, "I get him relaxed... give him exactly what he likes. Give him a nice line to stick up his nose. Then I tell him about you, old man... gets him kinda nervous.... He wants to know more, but he's scared shitless. But the more he thinks about it, the more he has to... like he's got no choice.... He wants to know about you. I want to know about Taylor. . . . I can't help him if I don't know what's been going on, can I? That's what I tell him . . . You got problems, man, tell them to Reno. You got confessions, man, my lips are sealed. This is a scary dude, asking about Taylor, I tell him. Not a guy you can fuck around with. He's gonna throw your ass in jail, man, if you've been doing something you shouldn't. Call your daddy, tell him to get the bail money ready . . . And shit, old man, if this little fucker doesn't start talking . . . Tells me he set Taylor up, gave him something to do, taking important pictures, learning to develop them. Something to do with computers. And, of course, I know the little fucker now. I've seen the paintings. This ain't no goody-two-shoes talking. This ain't no social worker. This guy's got some kind of piddly-ass scam going *using* Taylor . . . and now acting all righteous, like he was teaching him some kind of skill. Must have shit his pants when he finds out Taylor was taking pictures for the Angel too. Blackmailing some old men and splitting the profit. Rob wants him to stop—and they get into an argument. It must have been a doozy. . . . Taylor tells him he's got enough money now—if he wanted to, he could leave for good. And when Rob was telling me this, he started laughing weird, like he didn't know I was there anymore—'Could just take her and split, Taylor said'—Rob gets up and takes a big swig of brandy. Says the next day Taylor was dead and had hidden all the pictures. Rob says he don't care anymore if he didn't find them—he just didn't want anyone else to find them."

Over the kid's tense body, Angelo met Bryce's eyes sadly.

"Then Rob says if someone's snooping around, he wants to clean out Taylor's old place . . . gives me the address . . . tells me to destroy everything that was Taylor's—clothes, pictures, everything. And I say, *pictures*? Dude, I didn't think you had any pictures . . . And he said that blackmail stuff of the Angel's was there. . . . And then you know what he said?" Reno's grip on Bryce grew strong again. He struggled to raise himself; sweat beaded his face. "He said, and all that album junk he used to carry around . . . worthless crap . . ." Reno rasped. "Those pictures . . . a whole lifetime, whole other lives that Taylor put together . . . Didn't mean nothing to this jerkoff. . . . It wasn't in some fancy *gallery*."

Reno stared at Bryce as if in doing so, it gave him the power to make Bryce share his outrage, as if he could pass it along like a legacy. Then his grip slackened. Bryce caught his hand before it hit the ground. In the distance he could hear a siren.

"Don't know what happened to me. Went crazy, old man. Just went nuts," Reno whispered. "Grabbed some little gadget off the wall . . . started swinging . . . knocked the asshole flat on his butt. . . . The next thing I know, the Angel was there banging me up against the wall and it comes spilling out, old man. I tell him everything . . . I can't help it . . . and then the Angel is pissed." Reno licked the drops of sweat from his lips with a dry tongue. "Taylor introduced Rob and the Angel, I guess. After Taylor died, the Angel was looking for his cut of the collection, and Rob says he didn't know what he was talking about. So now the Angel is pissed because the guy's been fucking with him. He tells me to get out and get the pictures. Says he'll pay cash if his share's there and I can get outta town. So I split, old man . . . I don't know what happened after that. . . . But as you can see," he said, with a weak stab at humor, "the Angel don't like being fucked with."

Sirens screeched; red lights glanced off the columns of the Palace; men's voices echoed dully across the parking lot.

"Reno, which direction did he head?" Bryce asked.

"Kid like the Angel could be halfway across this city in five minutes," Angelo noted sourly.

Reno gave a weak laugh.

"The Angel ain't going nowhere. Not without his pictures. Probably tearing up every one of Mom's outhouses looking for them."

"Where are they?" Bryce pressed.

"Tellin' you for one reason, old man . . . Don't let him hurt my mom . . . she don't mean no harm . . . she's just weird, y'know . . . had a bad trip . . . never came down." His face was twisted abruptly with a spasm of pain that left him whimpering. "At the end . . . there's a path . . . Better watch it, old man, cause you never know. You could trip and fall on hard ground or trip and slide into the ocean. Top of the second . . . hill there's . . . cypress trees . . . make like a shelter . . . Mom's got a little fence of twigs around it . . . like a fucking *nest*. They're in there, old man. . . . It's one of the last. . . . You hurry, old man, you might be able to catch him." Reno's grin held for a moment. He said: "Better move those buns, old man. I'm scared enough as it is without you staring at me."

Bryce ran down the service road to the echo of Angelo's cries to one of his staff: "Follow that damn idiot, will you?"

But Bryce couldn't bother waiting. A storm was building; the city lights reflecting off the ceiling of clouds left light enough for him to navigate, if not with ease, at least with a certain degree of dexterity. He ran, listening for any sound out of tune with those created by the wind, watching for a shadow moving suddenly out of rhythm with those surrounding it, working to maintain his balance through the rocks and potholes. Once he jumped when he felt a branch touch his shoulder like a hand and his imagination supplied the slip of a knife between his ribs. And when he arrived at the top of the first rise, he was breathless and edgy.

He intended to move on, but the instinct that had worked with him thus far in his life kept him still just long enough to take a quick survey of the road ahead. It was here he felt the skin up the back of his spine prickle, where he caught a low moan hiding beneath that of the wind's. Ahead, just off the path to the right, he caught sight of the rubble. Toward this scab on the landscape he moved cautiously, preparing himself for what he might find.

A ten-pound bag of cat food had been slashed and its bowels

spilled over the dirt floor, where among the overturned tins and odd bits of clothing, magazine pictures of cats had been partially torn from the walls of the lean-to and flapped in the wind. Bryce was aware of the fear of being, once again, too late.

Outside the moaning played tricks on his ears. Right? No. Left? No. He marched straight. He knelt to move a large limb of ancient lilac to one side, and drew back suddenly.

Huddled inside the safety of a large abandoned drainpipe, he saw a face with the innocence of one whose cares are whittled down to one homely desire. She cowered, pulling her mismatched clothes closer to her body. The three white kittens in her lap protested her movement with small cries. Under different circumstances Bryce might have felt sad; or maybe the stench of her unwashed body might have given his stomach a turn. As it was, all he could feel was relief that Reno's mother was safe. He let the branch fall into place.

So the Angel had come this far. But how many huts had distracted him between here and the one that held the prize? Bryce moved on, thankful that the sound of his trek through the brush was swallowed by the storm and aware that the same circumstances that could work for him could also work against him.

The hilltop was a forest of cypress. Substantial trunks, white and bare; a canopy of greenery, upheld by limbs twisted like biceps, lats, and pectorals long overworked. Here the light was filtered, the ground barren of all but the most anemic growth. In front of him lay a dead branch about four feet long, sturdy and nearly straight. If applied with enough force, it could administer one hell of a concussion. He stopped and took it firmly in hand.

A nest, Reno had called it. And so it was. A few yards to the right of him, a copse of trees with a dark weave of twigs and cloth and paper high enough to reach past his waist stood, a thatch of dead shrubbery for a roof. From somewhere nearby came the guttural screech of a cat. Resigned to the unexpected and inevitably painful, Bryce pushed on. An old tire mat provided a flap for the door, and kneeling, he used the end of his stick to gently pull it back a few inches. Not at all gently, he felt the impact of a kick in the ribs, the jerk of his body as it hit the ground. He rolled with it. His assailant tried for a kick in the groin, but Bryce blocked it with one arm; with the other he grabbed the leg the man was balanced on. As he fell, Bryce could hear the click of a switchblade open.

They twisted, came up on their knees and, like wrestlers, stumbled to their feet. As he rose, Bryce's hand found his stick and he brought it up in one sharp, clean movement that sent the knife spinning out of the Angel's hand. Like an elaborate piece of choreography they had rehearsed, the Angel lifted his knee and hit Bryce's hand with enough force to send his stick into the air like a twirling baton.

Now both free of weapons, Bryce threw his body at the Angel's and they fell heavily. Bryce was good at these hand-to-hand encounters. They brought out the same sort of competitiveness in him he had experienced on the high school wrestling team. He wished he could see the Angel's face, to judge from the sweat there exactly where his greatest tension lay. There was no swearing, no talk; blending into the dirt and darkness, the man's face was nothing but a blur. Bryce had an eerie sense of wrestling with the unknown, the invisible; as if he wrestled with no one but himself. The Angel writhed between his thighs, clawed into Bryce's wrists with his fingers, bit him once in the shoulder, but other than that, he had no sense of who it was he held in his grasp. The Angel slipped through his legs, twisted and turned and tried to drive Bryce's Adam's apple to the back of his throat.

The ground dropped suddenly beneath them, and they rolled farther into the dark, greeted by a fresh burst of sea air unblocked by trees, by the boom of the water below them. God, where the hell was the cliff? Bryce shoved his fist into the Angel's hard stomach. With one hand the Angel tried to push Bryce's nose up into his brain. Bryce forced his hand off, and heard muffled shouts.

A second later Bryce called out in pain as the Angel fisted a rock into the only part of Bryce he could effectively reach, his ribs. Stunned, Bryce's hold weakened and the Angel slipped out from under him. Lights zigzagged erratically across the landscape. For a split second, as if exhausted, perhaps trying to decide whether to finish the job and use the rock on Bryce's head, the Angel lay beside him, gasping. But as Bryce regained his breath and strength, the Angel started up. Bryce made a grab for him, catching his arm and twisting it until he thought he felt it crack. The Angel jerked and fell. Bryce thought he heard a man scream "Hold it!" before something like fireworks exploded before his eyes and, as if by delayed reaction, crackled overhead.

The next thing Bryce knew he was sitting in a car next to Angelo, who sat with his forehead pressed against the top of the steering wheel, muttering: "Arizona, here I come."

Chapter Eighteen

■

"So that's how it was, boss," Angelo told his superior. Angelo always called him boss, though it was less a term of respect than a habit of speech. Angelo called his bartender boss too. Angelo's chief knew this, having on occasion frequented some of the same bars. "One picture collection, but three separate sets of pictures." Angelo held examples of each, letting them fall on the desk with a short flutter. "Pictures Taylor took for the Angel of some old men getting their money's worth. And wait until you see who's in there," Angelo said with a knowledgeable lift to his eyebrows. "Another set, wanted by Rob Gautier of his computer microchip theft. And number three, Taylor's collection of family photos, wanted by Reno for . . . sentimental reasons."

Angelo's chief leaned forward, folding his hands on his desk, watching Angelo twitching in the seat across from him. Angelo twitched a lot in the presence of this man—for the same reason he left half-smoked cigarettes burning all over the man's office, or even smiled at him in the hall. It was for the same reason a child prods a lizard with a stick—to get it to blink, to see if it would move.

"Taylor hides Rob Gautier's photos in the Palace to cause him a pain in the ass. The rest of his collection, including the Angel's photos, are tucked away in the apartment Rob Gautier owns, until, of course, Reno hunts them down and hides them in his mother's shack."

"I've read the report. Interesting," he said, without any inflection in his tone, with only a perfunctory blink.

Angelo sometimes wondered if this man did this to him on purpose.

"Oh, yeah, sure. *Interesting,*" Angelo said. "I mean—have you thought about this?—if Bryce hadn't gone talking to Reno, Reno wouldn't have gone to that exhibit, seen Roxanne Gautier's signature and thought it was Rob's. And wouldn't have gone to Rob Gautier's that night. And if he hadn't gone, the Angel wouldn't have known Rob had his photos. Shitty, isn't it? How do you think Paul Gautier feels right now for asking Bryce to look into his wife's paintings?" Angelo sat back, folded his hands on his lap and waited.

The man squinted. Angelo decided that this, technically, could not qualify as a response. Silently, slowly, he counted to thirty.

"I mean, all Gautier probably wanted to know was whether his wife was faithful. Maybe—*maybe*—give her some help if she's in a jam—and look at the can of worms he opens. You never know, do you? Seems simple. But now three people are dead. We've got Rob Gautier in the morgue, we got Reno in the morgue. We're still waiting for the Angel to wash up on shore, though." My God, am I getting hysterical? he thought.

The seat of the man across the desk creaked.

"Makes you wonder what kind of shit you're gonna cause just by walking down the street, doesn't it? You ever play dominoes? Ever see the way they—click!—go down one by one—"

"Angelo."

"Yes, boss."

The man was as deliberate as a chess move. ''If I understand you and the report correctly, Taylor Adams is dead, Rob Gautier is dead—in fact, everyone involved in criminal activity is now deceased.''

''You got it right, boss.''

''So there is no one living to hand over to the D.A. to prosecute, correct?''

''On target, boss.''

''Some of the microchip information might be of some small interest to certain other departments, but for *our* department—homicide—there is nothing left for us to do except file reports, correct? Justice, if that's what you want to call it, has more or less taken care of itself.''

Angelo shrugged.

The man picked up the pictures, shuffling through them idly, pausing briefly over one or two. He whistled through his teeth. ''Well then, that's nice, isn't it?''

Chapter Nineteen

■

Bryce was packing when the telephone rang. He continued packing, carefully folding sweaters and placing neat stacks of underwear in the corner of the case, as he listened to Angelo's wry summary on his physical condition.

". . . a knot on the head, a knot under the eye, and two bruised ribs," the policeman catalogued with undue cheerfulness. "And you won't go to the hospital. 'Just stick an Ace bandage on it and it'll be fine,' you say. Christ! Well, smart boy, how is it?"

"It's fine, Angelo," he deadpanned.

"Bullshit. You taking off this afternoon?"

"At five."

"Well, maybe your girlfriend can plaster you back together."

"She's very skillful," Bryce conceded.

"I bet," Angelo said, and managed to make it sound obscene. "Speaking of skill—just wanted to say thanks. Would have been a helluva lot more trouble for us if you hadn't had three quarters of it put together before we even started."

Bryce ignored this tribute by asking one of the questions most on his mind: "What are Reno's burial arrangements?"

"Tomorrow at eleven-thirty. Quiet, no funeral. I'm not sure his mother understands he's dead."

"Who's paying for it?"

"I took up a collection," Angelo said. "He was a favorite, of sorts."

"Did you get enough contributors?"

"What was that? Oh, yeah. Sure. *Plenty.*"

"I see," Bryce remarked dryly.

"It's Christmas. Makes people feel guilty." He spoke as one who was an authority on the subject of guilt. "They get generous."

"I see," Bryce repeated.

Apparently anxious to move the conversation on, Angelo said: "It's no wonder the Angel was so stubborn about getting his share of the collection. He had a fortune stored there. Juicy stuff. There will be a couple of fine, upstanding, supposedly straight citizens very happy to get them."

"Did you find the Angel yet?" asked Bryce. Frantic to get out of Bryce's grasp the Angel had cracked him over the head hard enough to knock him out, but, weakened by the pain of his wrenched arm, not hard enough to smash his skull; at the sound of the gun, he seemed to stop, suspended spiderlike at an angle from the cliff before disappearing into the dark mix of mist and sea below.

"Should have washed up somewhere by now, but so far, nothing." After a short pause, Angelo gave his last word on the subject. "Of course, you don't expect the Angel to die, you expect him to just dematerialize."

With four hours before his plane left, Bryce had time to indulge himself. In an act he didn't bother to excuse as part of the Christmas spirit, he sat down and wrote a large check to Angelo and had it sent with a note both humorous and obscene.

Then he strolled to Union Square to purchase a few small items: special jars of wine jelly from the Napa Valley for some neighbors he thought would enjoy them; a crock of sourdough starter for himself, just for the hell of it; two bottles of very good California champagne for James, who was still suspicious of the yeasty quality of the French ones; and a big box of See's candy, because he knew Katharine liked them. His real Christmas shopping was done. He just wanted to take a last look at the city preparing for a holiday. He dropped money in the cup of a legless man who sold pencils and some in the jar of an old woman. Maybe Angelo was right, he thought. And a good thing too. Reason enough for a holiday if it made you think of someone besides yourself.

He eventually found himself back on Sutter Street staring into the store window that held the apricot sweater. Standing in front of the display, he decided anyone but Katharine wearing it was unthinkable. He strode purposefully inside. It was a rare and brave act for him to purchase an item of women's clothing. He nearly fainted when they handed him the bill. And though he never actually considered not buying it, his hand hesitated ever so briefly before he handed over the traveler's checks.

Bryce returned to the hotel to find Laura had left a suitcase full of presents for James. Attached to the handle was a scribbled note: *Thanks so much, and wrap them for me once you're back, will you, darling?*

He had one more place to go. He gathered his bags and took a taxi to the Gautiers'.

At first he thought Kim wasn't going to let him in. But then Kim relented, telling the security man to allow him up, showing him into the living room, where Roxanne stood alone by the fireplace, in worn jeans and paint-smeared smock.

"I came to return this to you," he said, offering her the diary.

"Thank you," she replied, but made no move to accept it.

"And thank you for helping the police clear this up so quickly. As soon as things settle down, I'm sure Paul will let you know how grateful he is."

"Your book helped," he told her. He set it on the fireplace mantel.

"Did it? Well, I'm glad it was useful for something," she said.

"It was," he told her, and she looked at him doubtfully. "Is Paul here?" he asked.

"No," she said abruptly. "He's been spending a lot of time seeing to family matters since Rob was found."

"Of course," Bryce said, sensing that in the odd turn of events, he knew too many secrets, that she now wanted her confessor banished permanently behind the iron grail. He didn't imagine Paul felt much differently. "Well, then," he went on, unfailingly polite, "I'll be running along." He turned to go.

"Are you going back to Ireland today?" she asked suddenly, touching him lightly on the arm, surprising him. This ordinary gesture seemed personal in contrast to the rest of their conversation.

"I'm on my way to the airport now," he told her, and forgetting his ribs, moved just enough in the wrong way to make him wince.

"Are you hurt?"

"Just a little sore."

"Paul didn't do that, did he?" she asked, more curious than concerned.

"No."

Roxanne clicked her tongue like a disapproving mother. "Kevin, have you been boxing with God? I told you before—your arms are too short." She had a facility for knowing what to say to amuse. Bryce, indeed, did smile.

"No," he said. "Merely wrestling with an angel."

She took her book from the mantel and considered it. "Books are funny," she mused. "Sometimes one book seems just right, and then one day you realize that, well, maybe it no longer applies.'' She looked at Bryce. ''I've got a new book now.'' She reached into the pocket of her smock and took out a slim, brown volume, flashing it just long enough for Bryce to see, before replacing it. The book was Sartre's *No Exit*.

''No more Melville, no more Trollope?''

She shook her head delicately. ''No, no more.'' And to his horror, she dropped her own green bound book into the fire. ''Good-bye, Kevin,'' she said, and left the room.

Does art have any ethics? Bryce still didn't know. He got a poker and fished the diary out of the fire. He smothered the charred cover with his scarf, wrapped the book in his handkerchief and pocketed it.

So much, he mused, for my ethics.

At four o'clock that afternoon Roxanne marched down the wide walkway of the bridge to the first tower. The bridge swayed and rumbled under the weight of the rush-hour traffic. The wind blew in short, damp gusts. Occasionally a horn would honk or a driver would call rudely to her as he drove by. Unconsciously she toyed with the problem of putting sound on canvas. She paced herself a distance from the rail. The height made her nervous, and she longed to have her feet on more stable ground.

A Filipino man in a Cushman cart tooled slowly by and examined her as though he guessed she would be the bridge's next casualty and was readying himself for his description to the police. The cart passed and displayed another man in back who leered out at her horribly. A hefty woman jogged past in navy shorts. A thin man with hairy legs ignored the posted edict to walk his bicycle around the tower; he flew by at an alarming speed.

It amazed her that the few short steps around the tower could so deaden the traffic noise. Just a few steps into a different world with an illusion of isolation. A foghorn blew underneath her as she gripped the railing with both hands. She closed her eyes and swallowed hard. When she summoned the courage to open them again, she did not bother to gaze at the view of Alcatraz or of the Presidio or even at the picturesqueness of Sausalito. No, she had come for one purpose only, and she went at it determinedly, struggling with her vertigo. It was part of her passion for the proper details.

At the edge of the railing she tilted her head toward the water below, tossing and foaming, a mustardy green. It should be done in thick, thick oil that would swirl and cake, then be touched with the color of foam. Perhaps, too, a study in parles paint on paper . . .